THE LIFE OF THE CATERPILLAR

J. HENRI FABRE

TRANSLATED BY
ALEXANDER TEIXEIRA DE MATTOS
FELLOW OF THE ZOOLOGICAL SOCIETY OF LONDON

INTRODUCTION BY
ROYAL DIXON

BONI AND LIVERIGHT

PUBLISHERS :: :: NEW YORK

CONTENTS

INTRODUCTION

"EACH thing created," says Emerson, "has ᶠ its painter or its poet." Truly did insects find their painter, prophet and poet in Jean Henri Fabre. Perhaps no star arose to greet him on the day of his birth; but we should like to believe that myriads of tiny crickets, moths, wasps, and caterpillars had long awaited their Columbus. By his efforts a new world filled with tiny, fascinating lives was discovered.

This prophet of nature spent much of his time near the little village of Serignan. From his earliest childhood he was fond of nature. Yet when the time came for him to decide upon a profession he chose the teaching of mathematics. His first position was at the college in Ajaccio. Here he made a warm friend of one of the professors, a famous botanist, who soon interested him anew in nature. Later he was appointed a professor of mathematics at the Lycée in Avignon, where he was able to spend considerable time with his nature work. In 1865 his genius began to be recognized. Under

Introduction

the empire he was given the decoration of honor for original work, and was offered the position of instructor to the Prince Imperial. This he did not accept, as it would have prevented him from carrying on his original researches.

He had married young, and the care of the family demanded that he remain in his profession. For many years he struggled with poverty, longing for the day when he would be able to spend all his time with his beloved insects. Yet he never complained, but always stayed hopeful and unspoiled by the rebuffs and discouragements that he met. Finally, at the age of sixty, he bought four acres of land near Serignan, were his long-held dream was to materialize. He built a little six-room cottage and laid out a garden.

Here the myriads of tiny creatures he so loved made their homes, and the water insects found a paradise among the reeds and rushes. "The wish is realized," he wrote. "It is a little late, O my pretty insects! Is the time remaining enough, O my busy Hymenoptera, to enable me to add yet a few pages to your history, or will my failing strength cheat my good intentions?" It was,

Introduction

indeed, the eleventh hour; yet he was able to tell many more stories of the insects.

In this tiny garden spot, remote from the world, which he called his harmas, his "lavatory of living entomology," teeming with herbs and thistles, and swarming with hosts of insects, he could study and experiment to his heart's content. For he was hidden behind high walls, with only the creatures he most enjoyed, remote from curious eyes and all humans except the beloved members of his own family and a few peasant friends. For days he would wander out on the hills to watch the caterpillars or "the dung-beetle rolling his football, and the tarantula holding his wallet of eggs to the sun; await for hours the return of a wasp to an infinitesimal hole in the sand; rejoice over a donkey's hoof-print in the clay, turned by a shower into 'an aquarium worth the finest inventions of the laboratories.'" But he never wearied in his observations and it was from these that he was enabled to publish his colossal series of "Souvenirs Entomologiques"; and later bring out nine volumes, including "The Life of the Caterpillar."

And who can write such a masterpiece

Introduction

without work?   Like Carlyle, he believed
that "work is worship," and when advising
his younger brother, whom he greatly loved,
he said: "Science, Frederic, knowledge is
everything. You are too good a thinker not
to say with me that no one can better employ
his time than acquiring fresh knowledge.
. . . Work, then, when you have the opportunity that very few may possess, and for
which you ought to be only too thankful."

The real Fabre may be best seen through
his own work and letters; and we get an
excellent picture of this great-hearted child
of nature through his own words to his
brother about his own methods of study.
"You choose a quiet retreat where the light
is not too strong. There you are, elbows on
the table, your thumbs are to your ears, and
a book in front of you. The intelligence
awakens; the will holds the rein of it; the
outer world disappears, the ear no longer
hears, the eye no longer sees, the body no
longer exists: the mind . . . recollects itself; . . . its insight increases. The hours
pass quickly; time has no measure. What a
day, great God! But hosts of truth are
grouped in the memory; the difficulties which

Introduction

checked you yesterday have fused in the fire
of reflection; volumes have been devoured,
and you are content with your day. . . .
Above all, you must not be discouraged; time
is nothing provided the will is alert; . . .
strength, and perseverance, and you will see
nothing is impossible."

Surely it was not to his genius! For he
realized at the beginning of his work that
he had to get truth as all artists do—through
his own observations and by hard mental
work. No ready-made, hand-me-down decisions for him! He would seek and see for
himself. He hated libraries, museums, and
chairs of learning; yet this was partially due,
no doubt, to his intense desire for the out-
doors, and also to the fact that until past his
prime he scarcely went beyond the medieval
walls of Avignon. He had to be practically
compelled to go to Paris by the Minister of
Education to be decorated, rewarded, and
presented to the Emperor. After it was
over, he hastened away to "the incomparable
museum of the fields," notwithstanding the
Minister's insistence that he should at least
see the incomparable entomological collec-
tions of Paris. For forty years he had

Introduction

struggled to win freedom for his "slow and delicate studies."

Little wonder that this genius for patience should be the author of "The Life of the Caterpillar." For what years of work, of patience, of seeking for the truth was required! His disdain for the commonly accepted theories of the day caused him to pay little attention to the published observations of other naturalists; and too, he wished to have first-hand information on all subjects about which he wrote. This is why in "The Life of the Caterpillar" we see the Pine Processionary portrayed in such tender, human terms, and with such scientific accuracy that even a child may be led into this insect wonderland. Here one may marvel at the Pine Processionary as she works and lives among her many neighbors in a community; at their processions, their methods of gathering food, of building tents for the cold wintry days, of their defensive powers. "Let us make a compact," he said to the Processionary Caterpillar of the Pine. " You have a story to tell. Tell it me; and for a year, for two years or longer, until I know more or less about it, I shall leave you undisturbed,

Introduction

even at the cost of lamentable suffering to the pines." Again in this book we are shown the private life of the Arbutus Caterpillar, of the Great Peacock, the Banded Monk, the Cabbage-Caterpillar. How marvelous is their picture! Little wonder that their biographer was a stoic, a rebel, and willing to battle for truth.

And battle it was, so far as people were concerned; for he cared little for what they thought, and nothing for fame. This was for the "noisy and noxious." His only passion was for insects; and two words would have adequately described him—*perseverance* and *kindness*. How strikingly characteristic of him is the story told by him in the *Souvenirs Entomologiques* of how he tried to find why the tufts of hair on certain caterpillars were poisonous. He applied the concentrated fluid not to an animal, but on himself—between his fingers and under his arm. Why? Perhaps he did not wish to destroy an animal! It was his kindness of heart. His was a work of love. And strangely enough, he seemed to have no theories nor time for attacking the theories of others. "He was not a maker of generalizations,"

Introduction

says one critic, "and came at last to distrust
them all, showing that minute details—apparently so trifling that they are disregarded
—are often the master-keys to the most
solemn questions men can consider."

While Darwin had called Fabre "that in-
imitable observer," yet Fabre did not agree
with his ideas of evolution. He emphasized
instinct among the insects, and called it "the
insect's genius." Every chapter in "The Life
of the Caterpillar" has something to say on
this matter. When speaking of the caterpillars' preparation for the winter weather,
he asks: "Do they foresee the future, these
wary ones who take such precautions against
the rigors of winter? Obviously not. Their
few months' experience—if indeed experience
can be mentioned in connection with a caterpillar—tells them of savory bellyfuls of green
stuff, of gentle slumbers in the sun on the
terrace of the nest; but nothing hitherto has
made them acquainted with cold, steady rain,
with frost, snow and furious blasts of wind.
And these creatures, knowing naught of winter's woes, take the same precaution as if
they were thoroughly aware of all that the
inclement season holds in store for them."

Introduction

"Fabre," according to a writer in the London *Nation*, "seems destined to become an authority for the rebels against the whole system of accepted and orthodox science; nor is it a mere coincidence that those who attack prevailing conclusions based upon the Darwinian theory of natural selection find a mint of material in his investigations." He offered untold weapons, scientifically speaking, for them to battle with if they so desired; yet himself made no use of these weapons to know the truth about the insects: their births, love affairs, occupations, strange transformations, and deaths, and this is why "The Life of the Caterpillar" is more fascinating than a novel.

Today he is fast becoming one of the greatest characters in French literature. The entire intellectual world pays homage to "the poet of science." Perhaps he stands alone in his century as the most patient and keen observer of the nature world. His praises have been sung by many of the world's greatest thinkers: Rostrand declared that "he was a savant who thinks like a philosopher and writes like a poet"; Maurice Maeterlinck thought him "one of the finest

Introduction

poets of the century that is past; while our
own young naturalist, Brayton Eddy, says:
"His books should compose a nature Bible!"
While Fabre never actually published more
than one volume of verse, yet he shows the
innate sympathy and delicacy of the poet in
all his nature writings. Maurice Maeterlinck's "The Life of the Bee" is said to have
been inspired by his talks with Fabre.

It was only the great minds and the simple
minds that seemed to understand Fabre.
And this is exactly what he wanted; for his
chief desire was to reach children and create
in them a love for natural history. This is
why he so carefully avoided the scientific
vocabulary which, too often he says, "seemed
borrowed from some Iroquois idiom." He
hated big words, expressing his thoughts
with a simplicity and charm that is rarely
equalled.

His fame came late, so very late that he
seemed a bit dazed at the sudden attention
heaped upon him. He cared nothing for it
except in so much as it secured for him more
time for his beloved research. He was already an old man when the French Govern-
ment was awakened to the fact that he was

Introduction

a great man and had done a colossal work in a most distinguished manner. A modest pension was bestowed upon him for his declining years. This relieved him of all anxiety, and the fates had left him a lovely daughter to be near him as he sat in the old rustic chair in his garden at Serignan.

On his last birthday an old friend from Avignon visited him. It is to a letter from this friend, published in a Paris journal and quoted in *Review of Reviews,* that we are indebted for this glowing tribute. "We see the magnificent spectacle of an old man of whom the soul remains young, the mind clear, from whose lips you hear no word that resembles a complaint, and now who takes the road to the end without regrets and with serene resignation."

ROYAL DIXON.

Houston, Texas,
April 1, 1925.

CHAPTER I

THE PINE PROCESSIONARY: THE EGGS
AND THE HATCHING

THIS caterpillar has already had his story told by Réaumur,[1] but it was a story marked by gaps. These were inevitable in the conditions under which the great man worked, for he had to receive all his materials by barge from the distant Bordeaux Landes. The transplanted insect could not be expected to furnish its biographer with other than fragmentary evidence, very weak in those biological details which form the principal charm of entomology. To study the habits of insects one must observe them long and closely on their native heath, so to speak, in the place where their instincts have full and natural play.

With caterpillars foreign to the Paris climate and brought from the other end of France, Réaumur therefore ran the risk of

[1] René Antoine Ferchault de Réaumur (1683-1757), inventor of the Réaumur thermometer and author of *Mémoires pour servir à l'histoire naturelle des insectes.* —*Translator's Note.*

9

The Life of the Caterpillar

missing many most interesting facts. This is what actually happened, just as it did on a later occasion in the case of another alien, the Cicada.[1] Nevertheless, the information which he was able to extract from a few nests sent to him from the Landes is of the highest value.

Better served than he by circumstances, I will take up afresh the story of the Processionary Caterpillar of the Pine. If the subject does not come up to my hopes, it will certainly not be for lack of materials. In my *harmas*[2] laboratory, now stocked with a few trees in addition to its bushes, stand some vigorous fir-trees, the Aleppo pine and the black Austrian pine, a substitute for that of the Landes. Every year the caterpillar takes possession of them and spins his great purses in their branches. In the interest of the leaves, which are horribly ravaged, as though there had been a fire, I am obliged each winter to make

[1] For the Cicada or *Cigale,* an insect remotely akin to the Grasshopper and found more particularly in the south of France, cf. *Social Life in the Insect World,* by J. H. Fabre, translated by Bernard Miall: chaps. i to iv. —*Translator's Note.*

[2] The *harmas* was the enclosed piece of waste ground in which the author used to study his insects in their natural state.—*Translator's Note.*

The Processionary: the Eggs

a strict survey and to extirpate the nests with a long forked batten.

You voracious little creatures, if I let you have your way, I should soon be robbed of the murmur of my once so leafy pines! To-day I will seek compensation for all the trouble I have taken. Let us make a compact. You have a story to tell. Tell it me; and for a year, for two years or longer, until I know more or less all about it, I shall leave you undisturbed, even at the cost of lamentable suffering to the pines.

Having concluded the treaty and left the caterpillars in peace, I soon have abundant material for my observations. In return for my indulgence I get some thirty nests within a few steps of my door. If the collection were not large enough, the pine-trees in the neighbourhood would supply me with any necessary additions. But I have a preference and a decided preference for the population of my own enclosure, whose nocturnal habits are much easier to observe by lantern-light. With such treasures daily before my eyes, at any time that I wish and under natural conditions, I cannot fail to see the Processionary's story unfolded at full length. Let us try.

The Life of the Caterpillar

And first of all the egg, which Réaumur did not see. In the first fortnight of August, let us inspect the lower branches of the pines, on a level with our eyes. If we pay the least attention, we soon discover, here and there, on the foliage, certain little whitish cylinders spotting the dark green. These are the Bombyx' eggs: each cylinder is the cluster laid by one mother.

The pine-needles are grouped in twos. Each pair is wrapped at its base in a cylindrical muff which measures about an inch long by a fifth or sixth of an inch wide. This muff, which has a silky appearance and is white slightly tinted with russet, is covered with scales that overlap after the manner of the tiles on a roof; and yet their arrangement, though fairly regular, is by no means geometrical. The general aspect is more or less that of an immature walnut-catkin.

The scales are almost oval in form, semi-transparent and white, with a touch of brown at the base and of russet at the tip. They are free at the lower end, which tapers slightly, but firmly fixed at the upper end, which is wider and blunter. You cannot detach them either by blowing on them or by

The Processionary: the Eggs

rubbing them repeatedly with a hair-pencil. They stand up, like a fleece stroked the wrong way, if the sheath is rubbed gently upwards, and retain this bristling position indefinitely; they resume their original arrangement when the friction is in the opposite direction. At the same time, they are as soft as velvet to the touch. Carefully laid one upon the other, they form a roof that protects the eggs. It is impossible for a drop of rain or dew to penetrate under this shelter of soft tiles.

The origin of this defensive covering is self-evident: the mother has stripped a part of her body to protect her eggs. Like the Eider-duck, she has made a warm overcoat for them out of her own down. Réaumur had already suspected as much from a very curious peculiarity of the Moth. Let me quote the passage:

"The females," he says, "have a shiny patch on the upper part of their body, near the hind-quarters. The shape and gloss of this disk attracted my attention the first time that I saw it. I was holding a pin, with which I touched it, to examine its structure. The

contact of the pin produced a little spectacle
that surprised me: I saw a cloud of tiny
spangles at once detach themselves. These
spangles scattered in every direction: some
seemed to be shot into the air, others to the
sides; but the greater part of the cloud fell
softly to the ground.

"Each of those bodies which I am calling
spangles is an extremely slender lamina, bearing some resemblance to the atoms of dust
on the Moths' wings, but of course much big-
ger. . . . The disk that is so noticeable on
the hind-quarters of these Moths is therefore a heap—and an enormous heap—of
these scales. . . . The females seem to use
them to wrap their eggs in; but the Moths of
the Pine Caterpillar refused to lay while in my
charge and consequently did not enlighten me
as to whether they use the scales to cover
their eggs or as to what they are doing with
all those scales gathered round their hinder
part, which were not given them and placed
in that position to serve no purpose."

You were right, my learned master: that
dense and regular crop of spangles did not
grow on the Moth's tail for nothing. Is

The Processionary: the Eggs

there anything that has no object? You did
not think so; I do not think so either. Everything has its reason for existing. Yes, you
were well-inspired when you foresaw that the
cloud of scales which flew out under the point
of your pin must serve to protect the eggs.

I remove the scaly fleece with my pincers
and, as I expected, the eggs appear, looking
like little white-enamel beads. Clustering
closely together, they make nine longitudinal
rows. In one of these rows I count thirty-
five eggs. As the nine rows are very nearly
alike, the contents of the cylinder amount in
all to about three hundred eggs, a respectable
family for one mother!

The eggs of one row or file alternate
exactly with those in the two adjoining files,
so as to leave no empty spaces. They suggest a piece of bead-work produced with exquisite dexterity by patient fingers. It would
be more correct still to compare them with
a cob of Indian corn, with its neat rows of
seeds, but a greatly reduced cob, the tininess
of whose dimensions makes its mathematical
precision all the more remarkable. The
grains of the Moth's spike have a slight tend-
ency to be hexagonal, because of their mu-

tual pressure; they are stuck close together, so much so that they cannot be separated. If force is used, the layer comes off the leaf in fragments, in small cakes always consisting of several eggs apiece. The beads laid are therefore fastened together by a glutinous varnish; and it is on this varnish that the broad base of the defensive scales is fixed.

It would be interesting, if a favourable opportunity occurred, to see how the mother achieves that beautifully regular arrangement of the eggs and also how, as soon as she has laid one, all sticky with varnish, she makes a roof for it with a few scales removed one by one from her hind-quarters. For the moment, the very structure of the finished work tells us the course of the procedure. It is evident that the eggs are not laid in longitudinal files, but in circular rows, in rings, which lie one above the other, alternating their grains. The laying begins at the bottom, near the lower end of the double pine-leaf; it finishes at the top. The first eggs in order of date are those of the bottom ring; the last are those of the top ring. The arrangement of the scales, all in a longitudinal direction and attached by the end facing the

The Processionary; the Eggs

top of the leaf, makes any other method of progression inadmissible.

Let us consider in the light of reflection the elegant edifice now before our eyes. Young or old, cultured or ignorant, we shall all, on seeing the Bombyx' pretty little spike, exclaim:

"How handsome!"

And what will strike us most will be not the beautiful enamel pearls, but the way in which they are put together with such geometrical regularity. Whence we can draw a great moral, to wit, that an exquisite order governs the work of a creature without consciousness, one of the humblest of the humble. A paltry Moth follows the harmonious laws of order.

If Micromégas[1] took it into his head to leave Sirius once more and visit our planet, would he find anything to admire among us? Voltaire shows him to us using one of the diamonds of his necklace as a magnifying-glass in order to obtain some sort of view of the three-master which has run aground on his thumb-nail. He enters into conversation

[1]The eponymous hero of Voltaire's story of "the little great man," published in 1752 in imitation of *Gulliver's Travels.—Translator's Note.*

The Life of the Caterpillar

with the crew. A nail-paring, curved like a
horn, encompasses the ship and serves as a
speaking-trumpet; a tooth-pick, which touches
the vessel with its tapering end and the lips
of the giant, some thousand fathoms above,
with the other, serves as a telephone. The
outcome of the famous dialogue is that, if we
would form a sound judgment of things and
see them under fresh aspects, there is nothing
like changing one's planet.

The probability then is that the Sirian
would have had a rather poor notion of our
artistic beauties. To him our masterpieces
of statuary, even though sprung from the
chisel of a Phidias, would be mere dolls of
marble or bronze, hardly more worthy of interest than the children's rubber dolls are to
us; our landscape-paintings would be regarded as dishes of spinach smelling unpleas-
antly of oil; our opera-scores would be described as very expensive noises.

These things, belonging to the domain of
the senses, possess a relative æsthetic value,
subordinated to the organism that judges
them. Certainly the Venus of Melos and the
Apollo Belvedere are superb works; but even
so it takes a special eye to appreciate them.

The Processionary: the Eggs

Micromégas, if he saw them, would be full of pity for the leanness of human forms. To him the beautiful calls for something other than our sorry, frog-like anatomy.

Show him, on the other hand, that sort of abortive windmill by means of which Pythagoras, echoing the wise men of Egypt, teaches us the fundamental properties of the right-angled triangle. Should the good giant, contrary to our expectation, happen not to know about it, explain to him what the windmill means. Once the light has entered his mind, he will find, just as we do, that there is beauty there, real beauty, not certainly in that horrible hieroglyphic, the figure, but in the unchangeable relation between the lengths of the three sides; he will admire as much as we do geometry the eternal balancer of space.

There is, therefore, a severe beauty, belonging to the domain of reason, the same in every world, the same under every sun, whether the suns be single or many, white or red, blue or yellow. This universal beauty is order. Everything is done by weight and measure, a great statement whose truth breaks upon us all the more vividly as we probe more deeply into the mystery of things.

The Life of the Caterpillar

Is this order, upon which the equilibrium of the universe is based, the predestined result of a blind mechanism? Does it enter into the plans of an Eternal Geometer, as Plato had it? Is it the ideal of a supreme lover of beauty, which would explain everything?

Why all this regularity in the curve of the petals of a flower, why all this elegance in the chasings on a Beetle's wing-cases? Is that infinite grace, even in the tiniest details, compatible with the brutality of uncontrolled forces? One might as well attribute the artist's exquisite medallion to the steam-hammer which makes the slag sweat in the melting.

These are very lofty thoughts concerning a miserable cylinder which will bear a crop of caterpillars. It cannot be helped. The moment one tries to dig out the least detail of things, up starts a why which scientific investigation is unable to answer. The riddle of the world has certainly its explanation otherwhere than in the little truths of our laboratories. But let us leave Micromégas to philosophize and return to the commonplaces of observation.

The Pine Bombyx has rivals in the art of

The Processionary: the Eggs

gracefully grouping her egg-beads. Among their number is the Neustrian Bombyx, whose caterpillar is known by the name of "Livery," because of his costume. Her eggs are assembled in bracelets around little branches varying greatly in nature, apple- and pear-branches chiefly. Any one seeing this elegant work for the first time would be ready to attribute it to the fingers of a skilled stringer of beads. My small son Paul opens eyes wide with surprise and utters an astonished "Oh!" each time that he comes upon the dear little bracelet. The beauty of order forces itself upon his dawning attention.

Though not so long and marked above all by the absence of any wrapper, the ring of the Neustrian Bombyx reminds one of the other's cylinder, stripped of its scaly covering. It would be easy to multiply these instances of elegant grouping, contrived now in one way, now in another, but always with consummate art. It would take up too much time, however. Let us keep to the Pine Bombyx.

The hatching takes place in September, a little earlier in one case, a little later in another. So that I may easily watch the new-born caterpillars in their first labours, I have

The Life of the Caterpillar

placed a few egg-laden branches in the window of my study. They are standing in a glass of water which will keep them properly fresh for some time.

The little caterpillars leave the egg in the morning, at about eight o'clock. If I just lift the scales of the cylinder in process of hatching, I see black heads appear, which nibble and burst and push back the torn ceilings. The tiny creatures emerge slowly, some here and some there, all over the surface.

After the hatching, the scaly cylinder is as regular and as fresh in appearance as if it were still inhabited. We do not perceive that it is deserted until we raise the spangles. The eggs, still arranged in regular rows, are now so many yawning goblets of a slightly translucent white; they lack the cap-shaped lid, which has been rent and destroyed by the new-born grubs.

The puny creatures measure a millimetre[1] at most in length. Devoid as yet of the bright red that will soon be their adornment, they are pale-yellow, bristling with hairs, some shortish and black, others rather longer and white. The head, of a glossy black, is big

[1].039 inch.—*Translator's Note.*

in proportion. Its diameter is twice that of
the body. This exaggerated size of the head
implies a corresponding strength of jaw,
capable of attacking tough food from the
start. A huge head, stoutly clad in horn, is
the predominant feature of the budding caterpillar.

These macrocephalous ones are, as we see,
well-armed against the hardness of the pine-
needles, so well-armed in fact that the meal
begins almost immediately. After roaming
for a few moments at random among the
scales of the common cradle, most of the
young caterpillars make for the double leaf
that served as an axis for the native cylinder
and spread themselves over it at length.
Others go to the adjacent leaves. Here
as well as there they fall to; and the gnawed
leaf is hollowed into faint and very narrow
grooves, bounded by the veins, which are left
intact.

From time to time, three or four who have
eaten their fill fall into line and walk in step,
but soon separate, each going his own way.
This is practice for the coming processions.
If I disturb them ever so little, they sway
the front half of their bodies and wag their

heads with a jerky movement similar to the action of an intermittent spring.

But the sun reaches the corner of the window where the careful rearing is in progress. Then, sufficiently refreshed, the little family retreats to its native soil, the base of the double leaf, gathers into an irregular group and begins to spin. Its work is a gauze globule of extreme delicacy, supported on some of the neighbouring leaves. Under this tent, a very wide-meshed net, a siesta is taken during the hottest and brightest part of the day. In the afternoon, when the sun has gone from the window, the flock leaves its shelter, disperses around, sometimes forming a little procession within a radius of an inch, and starts browsing again.

Thus the very moment of hatching proclaims talents which age will develop without adding to their number. In less than an hour from the bursting of the egg, the caterpillar is both a processionary and a spinner. He also flees the light when taking refreshment. We shall soon find him visiting his grazing-grounds only at night.

The spinner is very feeble, but so active that in twenty-four hours the silken globe at-

The Processionary: the Hatching

tains the bulk of a hazel-nut and in a couple
of weeks that of an apple. Nevertheless, it
is not the nucleus of the great establishment
in which the winter is to be spent. It is a
provisional shelter, very light and inexpensive
in materials. The mildness of the season
makes anything else unnecessary. The young
caterpillars freely gnaw the logs, the poles between which the threads are stretched, that is
to say, the leaves contained within the silken
tent. Their house supplies them at the same
time with board and lodging. This excellent arrangement saves them from having to go out,
a dangerous proceeding at their age. For these
puny ones, the hammock is also the larder.

Nibbled down to their veins, the supporting
leaves wither and easily come unfastened from
the branches; and the silken globe becomes a
hovel that crumbles with the first gust of
wind. The family then moves on and goes
elsewhere to erect a new tent, lasting no longer
than the first. Even so does the Arab move
on, as the pastures around his camel-hide
dwelling become exhausted. These temporary
establishments are renewed several times over,
always at greater heights than the last, so
much so that the tribe, which was hatched on

The Life of the Caterpillar

the lower branches trailing on the ground, gradually reaches the higher boughs and sometimes the very summit of the pine-tree.

In a few weeks' time, a first moult replaces the humble fleece of the start, which is pale-coloured, shaggy and ugly, by another which lacks neither richness nor elegance. On the dorsal surface, the various segments, excepting the first three, are adorned with a mosaic of six little bare patches, of a bright red, which stand out a little above the dark background of the skin. Two, the largest, are in front, two behind and one, almost dot-shaped, on either side of the quadrilateral. The whole is surrounded by a palisade of scarlet bristles, divergent and lying almost flat. The other hairs, those of the belly and sides, are longer and whitish.

In the centre of this crimson marquetry stand two clusters of very short bristles, gathered into flattened tufts which gleam in the sun like specks of gold. The length of the caterpillar is now about two centimetres[1] and his width three or four millimetres.[2] Such is the costume of middle age, which, like the earlier one, was unknown to Réaumur.

[1] About three-quarters of an inch.—*Translator's Note.*
[2] .117 to .156 inch.—*Translator's Note.*

CHAPTER II

THE PINE PROCESSIONARY: THE NEST; THE COMMUNITY

NOVEMBER arrives, however, bringing cold weather; the time has come to build the stout winter tabernacle. High up in the pine the tip of a bough is chosen, with suitably close-packed and convergent leaves. The spinners surround it with a spreading network, which bends the adjacent leaves a little nearer and ends by incorporating them into the fabric. In this way they obtain an enclosure half silk, half leaves, capable of withstanding the inclemencies of the weather.

Early in December the work has increased to the size of a man's two fists or more. In its ultimate perfection, it attains a volume of nearly half a gallon by the end of winter.

It is roughly egg-shaped, tapering to a certain length below and extended into a sheath which envelops the supporting branch. The origin of this silky extension is as follows: every evening between seven and nine o'clock,

The Life of the Caterpillar

weather permitting, the caterpillars leave the nest and go down the bare part of the bough which forms the pole of the tent. The road is broad, for this axis is sometimes as wide as the neck of a claret-bottle. The descent is accomplished without any attempt at order and always slowly, so much so that the first caterpillars to come out have not yet dispersed before they are caught up by the others. The branch is thus covered by a continuous bark of caterpillars, made up of the whole community, which gradually divides into squads and disperses to this side and that on the nearest branches to crop their leaves. Now not one of the caterpillars moves a step without working his spinneret. Therefore the broad downward path, which on the way back will be the ascending path, is covered, as the result of constant traffic, with a multitude of threads forming an unbroken sheath.

It is obvious that this sheath, in which each caterpillar, passing backwards and forwards on his nocturnal rambles, leaves a double thread, is not an indicator laid down with the sole object of simplifying the journey back to the nest: a mere ribbon would be enough for that. Its use might well be to strengthen the edifice, to give it deeper foundations and to join it by a multitude of cables to the steady branch.

The whole thing thus consists, above, of the home distended into an ovoid and, below, of the stalk, the sheath surrounding the support and adding its resistance to that of the numerous other fastenings.

Each nest that has not yet had its shape altered by the prolonged residence of the caterpillars shows in the centre a bulky, milk-white shell, with around it a wrapper of diaphanous gauze. The central mass, formed of thickly-woven threads, has for a wall a thick quilt into which are absorbed, as supports, numbers of leaves, green and intact. The thickness of this wall may be anything up to three-quarters of an inch.

At the top of the dome are round openings, varying greatly in number and distribution, as wide across as an ordinary lead-pencil. These are the doors of the house, through which the caterpillars go in and out. All around the shell are projecting leaves, which the insects' teeth have respected. From the tip of each leaf there radiate, in graceful, undulating curves, threads which, loosely interlaced, form a light tent, a spacious verandah of careful workmanship, especially in the upper part. Here we find a broad terrace on which, in the daytime, the caterpillars come and doze in the sun, heaped one upon the other, with rounded backs. The network stretching overhead does duty as an awning: it moderates the heat of the sun's rays; it also saves the sleepers from a fall when the bough rocks in the wind.

Let us take our scissors and rip open the nest from end to end longitudinally. A wide window opens and allows us to see the arrangement of the inside. The first thing to strike us is that the leaves contained in the enclosure are intact and quite sound. The young caterpillars in their temporary establishments gnaw the leaves within the silken wrapper to death; they thus have their larder stocked for a few days without having to quit their shelter in bad weather, a condition made necessary by their weakness. When they grow stronger and start working on their winter home, they are very careful not to touch the leaves. Why these new scruples?

The reason is evident. If bruised, those leaves, the framework of the house, would

The Processionary: the Nest

very soon wither and then be blown off with
the first breath of wind. The silken purse,
torn from its base, would collapse. On the
other hand, if the leaves are respected, they
remain vigorous and furnish a stout support
against the assaults of winter. A solid fastening is superfluous for the summer tent,
which lasts but a day; it is indispensable to
the permanent shelter which will have to bear
the burden of heavy snows and the buffeting
of icy winds. Fully alive to these perils, the
spinner of the pine-tree considers himself
bound, however importunate his hunger,
not to saw through the rafters of his
house.

Inside the nest, therefore, opened by my
scissors I see a thick arcade of green leaves,
more or less closely wrapped in a silky sheath
whence dangle shreds of cast skin and strings
of dried droppings. In short, this interior
is an extremely unpleasant place, a rag-shop
and a sewage-farm in one, and corresponds
in no way with the imposing exterior. All
around is a solid wall of quilting and of
closely-woven leaves. There are no chambers, no compartments marked off by parti-
tion-walls. It is a single room, turned into a

labyrinth by the colonnade of green leaves placed in rows one above the other throughout the oval hall. Here the caterpillars stay when resting, gathered on the columns, heaped in confused masses.

When we remove the hopeless tangle at the top, we see the light filtering in at certain points of the roof. These luminous points correspond with the openings that communicate with the outer air. The network that forms a wrapper to the nest has no special exits. To pass through it in either direction, the caterpillars have only to push the sparse threads aside slightly. The inner wall, a compact rampart, has its doors; the flimsy outer veil has none.

It is in the morning, at about ten o'clock, that the caterpillars leave their night-apartment and come to take the sun on their terrace, under the awning which the points of the leaves hold up at a distance. They spend the whole day there dozing. Motionless, heaped together, they steep themselves deliciously in warmth and from time to time betray their bliss by nodding and wagging their heads. At six or seven o'clock, when it grows dark, the sleepers awake, bestir themselves,

The Processionary: the Nest

separate and go their several ways over the surface of the nest.

We now behold an indeed delightful spectacle. Bright-red stripes meander in every direction over the white sheet of silk. One goes up, another comes down, a third moves aslant; others form a short procession. And, as they solemnly walk about in a splendid disorder, each glues to the ground which it covers the thread that constantly hangs from its lip.

Thus is the thickness of the shelter increased by a fine layer added immediately above the previous structure; thus is the dwelling strengthened by fresh supports. The adjoining green leaves are taken into the network and absorbed in the building. If the tiniest bit of them remains free, curves radiate from that point, increasing the size of the veil and fastening it at a greater distance. Every evening, therefore, for an hour or two, great animation reigns on the surface of the nest, if the weather permits; and the work of consolidating and thickening the structure is carried on with indefatigable zeal.

Do they foresee the future, these wary ones who take such precautions against the rigours of winter? Obviously not. Their few

months' experience—if indeed experience can
be mentioned in connection with a caterpillar
—tells them of savoury bellyfuls of green
stuff, of gentle slumbers in the sun on the terrace of the nest; but nothing hitherto has
made them acquainted with cold, steady rain,
with frost, snow and furious blasts of wind.
And these creatures, knowing naught of winter's woes, take the same precautions as if they
were thoroughly aware of all that the inclement season holds in store for them. They
work away at their house with an ardour that
seems to say:

"Oh, how nice and warm we shall be in
our beds here, nestling one against the other,
when the pine-tree swings aloft its frosted
candelabra! Let us work with a will! *Laboremus!*"

Yes, caterpillars, my friends, let us work
with a will, great and small, men and grubs
alike, so that we may fall asleep peacefully;
you with the torpor that makes way for your
transformation into Moths, we with that last
sleep which breaks off life only to renew it.
Laboremus!

Anxious to watch my caterpillars' habits in
detail, without having to sally forth by lan-

The Processionary: the Nest

tern-light, often in bad weather, to see what happens in the pine-trees at the end of the enclosure, I have installed half-a-dozen nests in a greenhouse, a modest, glazed shelter which, though hardly any warmer than the air outside, at least affords protection from the wind and rain. Fixed in the sand, at a height of about eighteen inches, by the base of the bough that serves as both an axis and a framework, each nest receives for rations a bundle of little pine-branches, which are renewed as soon as they are consumed. I take my lantern every evening and pay my boarders a visit. This is the way in which most of my facts are obtained.

After the day's work comes the evening meal. The caterpillars descend from the nest, adding a few more threads to the silvery sheath of the support, and reach the posy of fresh green stuff which is lying quite near. It is a magnificent sight to see the red-coated band lined up in twos and threes on each needle and in ranks so closely formed that the green sprigs of the bunch bend under the load.

The diners, all motionless, all poking their heads forward, nibble in silence, placidly. Their broad black foreheads gleam in the

35

The Life of the Caterpillar

rays of the lantern. A shower of granules
drops on the sand below. These are the
residues of easy-going stomachs, only too
ready to digest their food. By to-morrow
morning the soil will have disappeared under
a greenish layer of this intestinal hail. Yes,
indeed, it is a sight to see, one far more stimu-
lating than that of the Silk-worms' mess-room.
Young and old, we are all so much interested
in it that our evenings almost invariably end in
a visit to the greenhouse caterpillars.

The meal is prolonged far into the night.
Satisfied at last, some sooner, some later, they
go back to the nest, where for a little longer,
feeling their silk-glands filled, they continue
spinning on the surface. These hard workers
would scruple to cross the white carpet without contributing a few threads. It is getting
on for one or even two o'clock in the morning when the last of the band goes indoors.

My duty as a foster-father is daily to renew the bunch of sprigs, which are shorn to
the last leaf; on the other hand, my duty as
an historian is to enquire to what extent the
diet can be varied. The district supplies me
with Processionaries on the Scotch pine, the
maritime pine and the Aleppo pine indif-

The Processionary: the Nest

ferently, but never on the other Coniferæ.
Yet one would think that any resin-scented
leaf ought to suit. So says chemical analysis.

We must mistrust the chemist's retort when
it pokes its nose into the kitchen. It may succeed in making butter out of tallow-candles
and brandy out of potatoes; but, when it tells
us that the products are identical, we shall do
well to refuse these abominations. Science,
astonishingly rich as it is in poison, will never
provide us with anything fit to eat, because,
though the raw substance falls to a large extent within its domain, that same substance
escapes its methods the moment that it is
wanted organized, divided and subdivided indefinitely by the process of life, as needed
by the stomach, whose requirements are not
to be met by measured doses of our reagents.
The raw material of cell and fibre may perhaps be artificially obtained, some day; cell
and fibre themselves, never. There's the rub
with your chemical feeding.

The caterpillars loudly proclaim the insur-
mountable difficulty of the problem. Relying
on my chemical data, I offer them the different substitutes for the pine growing in my
enclosure: the spruce, the yew, the thuja, the

The Life of the Caterpillar

juniper, the cypress. What! Am I asking
them, Pine Caterpillars, to bite into that?
They will take good care not to, despite the
tempting resinous smell! They would die of
hunger rather than touch it! One conifer
and one only is excepted: the cedar. My
charges browse upon its leaves with no appreciable repugnance. Why the cedar and not
the others? I do not know. The caterpillar's stomach, fastidious as our own, has its
secrets.

Let us pass to other tests. I have just slit
open longitudinally a nest whose internal
structure I want to explore. Owing to the
natural shrinkage of the split swan's-down, the
cleft reaches two fingers' breadth in the centre
and tapers at the top and bottom. What will
the spinners do in the presence of such a
disaster? The operation is performed by day,
while the caterpillars are slumbering in heaps
upon the dome. As the living-room is deserted at this time, I can cut boldly with the
scissors without risk of damaging any part
of the population.

My ravages do not wake the sleepers: all
day long not one appears upon the breach.
This indifference looks as though it were due

The Processionary: the Nest

to the fact that the danger is not yet known.
Things will be different to-night, when the
busy work begins again. However dull they
may be, the caterpillars will certainly notice
that hugh window which freely admits the
deadly draughts of winter; and, possessing
any amount of padding, they will crowd
round the dangerous gap and stop it up in a
trice. Thus do we argue, forgetting the animal's intellectual darkness.

What really happens is that, when night
falls, the indifference of the caterpillars remains as great as ever. The breach in the
tent provokes not a sign of excitement. They
move to and fro on the surface of the nest;
they work, they spin as usual. There is no
change, absolutely none, in their behaviour.
When the road covered chances to bring some
of them to the brink of the ravine, we see
no alacrity on their part, no sign of anxiety,
no attempt to close up the two edges of the
slit. They simply strive to accomplish the
difficult crossing and to continue their stroll
as though they were walking on a perfect
web. And they manage it somehow or other,
by fixing the thread as far as the length of
their body permits.

The Life of the Caterpillar

Having once crossed the gulf, they pursue their way imperturbably, without stopping any more at the breach. Others come upon the scene and, using the threads already laid as foot-bridges, pass over the rent and walk on, leaving their own thread as they go. Thus the first night's work results in the laying over the cleft of a filmy gauze, hardly perceptible, but just sufficient for the traffic of the colony. The same thing is repeated on the nights that follow; and the crevice ends by being closed with a scanty sort of Spider's web. And that is all.

There is no improvement by the end of the winter. The window made by my scissors is still wide open, though thinly veiled; its black spindle shape shows from the top of the nest to the bottom. There is no darn in the split texture, no piece of swan's-down let in between the two edges to restore the roof to its original state. If the accident had happened in the open air and not under glass, the foolish spinners would probably have died of cold in their cracked house.

Twice renewed with the same results, this test proves that the Pine Caterpillars are not alive to the danger of their split dwelling.

The Processionary: the Nest

Expert spinners though they be, they seem as unconscious of the ruin of their work as the spools in a factory are of a broken thread. They could easily make good the damage by stopping up the breach with the silk that is lavished elsewhere without urgent need; they could weave upon it a material as thick and solid as the rest of the walls. But no, they placidly continue their habitual task; they spin as they spun yesterday and as they will spin to-morrow, strengthening the parts that are already strong, thickening what is already thick enough; and not one thinks of stopping the disastrous gap. To let a piece into that hole would mean weaving the tent all over again from the beginning; and no insect, however industrious, goes back to what it has already done.

I have often called attention to this feature in animal psychology; notably I have described the ineptitude of the caterpillar of the Great Peacock Moth.[1] When the experimenter lops the top off the complicated eel-trap which forms the pointed end of the cocoon, this caterpillar spends the silk remaining

[1] In the course of an essay on aberration of instinct in a certain Mason-wasp which is not yet translated into English.—*Translator's Note.*

The Life of the Caterpillar

to him in work of secondary importance, instead of making good the series of cones, each fitting into the other, which are so essential to the hermit's protection. He continues his normal task imperturbably, as though nothing out of the way had taken place. Even so does the spinner in the pine-tree act with his burst tent.

' Your foster-parent must perpetrate yet another piece of mischief, O my Processionary; but this time it shall be to your advantage! It does not take me long to perceive that the nests intended to last through the winter often contain a population much greater than that of the temporary shelters woven by the very young caterpillars. I also notice that, when they have attained their ultimate dimensions, these nests differ very considerably in size. The largest of them are equal to five or six of the smallest. What is the cause of these variations?

Certainly, if all the eggs turned out well, the scaly cylinder containing the laying of a single mother would be enough to fill a splendid purse: there are three hundred enamelled beads here for hatching. But in families which swarm unduly an enormous waste al-

The Processionary: the Community

ways takes places and restores the balance of
things; if the called are legion, the chosen are
a well thinned-out troop, as is proved by the
Cicada, the Praying Mantis[1] and the Cricket.

The Pine Processionary, another crucible
of organic matter of which various devourers
take advantage, is also reduced in numbers
immediately after the hatching. The delicate
mouthful has shrunk to a few dozens of sur-
vivors around the light globular network in
which the family passes the sunny autumn
days. Soon they will have to be thinking of
the stoutly-built winter tent. At such a time,
it would be a boon if they could be many, for
from union springs strength.

I suspect an easy method of fusion among
a few families. To serve them as a guide
in their peregrinations about the tree, the
caterpillars have their silk ribbon, which they
follow on their return, after describing a bend.
They may also miss it and strike another, one
differing in no respect from their own. This
new ribbon marks the way to some nest
situated in the neighbourhood. The strayed

[1] A predatory insect, akin to the Locusts and Crickets,
which, when at rest, adopts an attitude resembling that
of prayer. Cf. *Social Life in the Insect World;* chaps.
v to vii.—*Translator's Note.*

caterpillars, failing to distinguish it from their own ribbon, follow it conscientiously and in this manner end by reaching a strange dwelling. Suppose them to be peacefully received: what will happen?

Once fused, the several groups assembled by the accident of the path will form a powerful city, fitted to produce great works; the concerted weaklings will give rise to a strong, united body. This would explain the thickly-populated, bulky nests situated so near to others that have remained puny. The former would be the work of a syndicate incorporating the interests of spinners collected from different parts; the latter would belong to families left in isolation by the luck of the road.

It remains to be seen whether the chance-comers, guided by a strange ribbon, meet with a good reception in the new abode. The experiment is easily made upon the nests in the greenhouse. In the evening, at the hours devoted to grazing, I remove with a pruning-shears the different little branches covered with the population of one nest and lay them on the provisions of the neighbouring nest, which provisions are also overrun with cater-

The Processionary: the Community

pillars. Or I can make shorter work of it
by taking the whole bunch, well covered with
the troop, of the first pouch and planting it
right beside the bunch of the second, so that
the leaves of the two mingle a little at the
edges.

There is not the least quarrelling between
the real proprietors and the new arrivals.
Both go on peacefully browsing, as though
nothing had happened. And all without hesitation, when bed-time comes, make for the
nest, like brothers who have always lived together; all do some spinning before retiring
to rest, thicken the blanket a little and are
then swallowed up in the dormitory. By
repeating the same operation next day and, if
necessary, the day after, in order to collect
the laggards, I succeed without the slightest
difficulty in wholly depopulating the first nest
and transferring all its caterpillars to the
second.

I venture to do something better still. The
same method of transportation allows me to
quadruple the output of a spinning-mill by
adding to it the workers of three similar establishments. And, if I limit myself to this
increase, the reason is not that any confusion

manifests itself in this shifting of quarters, but that I see no bounds to my experiment, so cheerfully do the caterpillars accept any addition to their number. The more spinners, the more spinning: a very judicious rule of conduct.

Let us add that the caterpillars which have been transported cherish no regrets for their old house. They are quite at home with the others and make no attempt to regain the nest whence they were banished by my artifices. It is not the distance that discourages them, for the empty dwelling is only half a yard away at most. If, for the purpose of my studies, I wish to restock the deserted nest, I am obliged once more to resort to transportation, which invariably proves successful.

Later, in February, when an occasional fine day allows of long processions on the walls and the sand-covered shelf of the greenhouse, I am able to watch the fusing of two groups without personally intervening. All that I have to do is patiently to follow the evolutions of a file on the march. I see it sometimes, after leaving one nest, enter a different one, guided by some fortuitous

change of route. Thenceforward the strangers form part of the community on the same
footing as the others. In a like fashion, when
the caterpillars walk abroad upon the tree
at night, the scanty groups of the outset must
increase and gather the number of spinners
which an extensive building requires.

Everything for everybody. So says the
Pine Processionary, nibbling his leaves without quarrelling in the least over his neighbours' mouthfuls, or else entering—and being
always peacefully received—another's home
precisely as he would his own. Whether a
member of the tribe or a stranger, he finds
room in the refectory and room in the dormitory. The others' nest is his nest. The
others' grazing-ground is his grazing-ground,
in which he is entitled to his fair share, one
neither greater nor smaller than the share of
his habitual or casual companions.

Each for all and all for each. So says
the Processionary, who every evening spends
his little capital of silk on enlarging a shelter
that is often new to him. What would he do
with his puny skein, if alone? Hardly anything. But there are hundreds and hundreds
of them in the spinning-mill; and the result

The Life of the Caterpillar

of their infinitesimal contributions, woven into a common stuff, is a thick blanket capable of resisting the winter. In working for himself, each works for the others; and these on their side work as zealously for each. O lucky animals that know nothing of property, the mother of strife! O enviable cenobites, who practise the strictest communism!

These habits of the caterpillars invite a few reflections. Generous minds, richer in illusions than in logic, set communism before us as the sovran cure for human ills. Is it practicable among mankind? At all times there have been, there still are and there always will be, fortunately, associations in which it is possible to forget in common some small part of the hardships of life; but is it possible to generalize?

The caterpillars of the pine can give us much valuable information in this respect. Let us have no false shame: our material needs are shared by the animals; they struggle as we do to take part in the general banquet of the living; and the manner in which they solve the problem of existence is not to be despised. Let us then ask ourselves what

48

The Processionary: the Community

are the reasons that cause cenobitism to flourish among the Processionaries.

One answer suggests itself inevitably, to begin with: the food problem, that terrible dis-
turber of the world's tranquillity, is here non-
existent. Peace reigns as soon as the stomach
is certain of being filled without a struggle.
A pine-needle or even less suffices for the
caterpillar's meal; and that needle is always
there, waiting to be eaten, is there in inexhaustible numbers, almost on the threshold of
the home. When dinner-time arrives, we
caterpillars go out, we take the air, we walk
a little in procession; then, without laborious
seeking, without jealous rivalries, we seat ourselves at the banquet. The table is plentifully spread and will never be bare, so large
and generous is the pine; all that we need
do is, from one evening to the next, to move
our dining-room a little farther on. Consequently, there are no present and no future
cares on the subject of provisions: the caterpillar finds food to eat almost as easily as he
finds air to breathe.

The atmosphere feeds all creatures on air
with a bounty which it is not necessary to
crave. All unknown to itself, without the

agency of any effort or labour, the animal receives its share of the most vital of elements. The niggardly earth, on the contrary, surrenders its gifts only when laboriously forced. Not fruitful enough to satisfy every need, it leaves the division of the food to the fierce eagerness of competition.

The mouthful to be procured engenders war between consumers. Look at two Ground-beetles coming at the same time upon a bit of Earth-worm. Which of the two shall have the morsel? The matter shall be decided by battle, desperate, ferocious battle. With these famished ones, who eat at long intervals and do not always eat their fill, communal life is out of the question.

The Pine Caterpillar is free from these woes. He finds the earth as generous as the atmosphere; he finds eating as easy as breathing. Other instances of perfect communism might be named. All occur among species living on a vegetable diet, provided however that victuals are plentiful and obtainable without a hard search. An animal diet, on the contrary, a prey, always more or less difficult to secure, banishes cenobitism. Where the portion is too small for one, what excuse would there be for guests?

The Pine Processionary knows nothing of privation. He knows as little of family ties, another source of unrelenting competition. To make ourselves a place in the sun is but a half of the struggle imposed upon us by life: we must also, as far as possible, prepare a place for our successors; and, as the preservation of the species is of greater importance than that of the individual, the struggle for the future is even fiercer than the struggle for the present. Every mother regards the welfare of her offspring as her primary law. Perish all else, provided that the brood flourish! Every one for himself is her maxim, imposed by the rigours of the general conflict; every one for himself is her rule, the safeguard of the future.

With maternity and its imperious duties, communism ceases to be practicable. At first sight, certain Hymenoptera[1] seem to declare the contrary. We find, for instance, the Mason-bees of the Sheds[2] nesting in myriads

[1] The order of insects embracing the Bees, Wasps, Ants, Saw-flies, Ichneumon-flies, etc.—*Translator's Note.*

[2] Cf. *The Mason-bees,* by J. Henri Fabre, translated by Alexander Teixeira de Mattos, *passim.—Translator's Note.*

on the same tiles and building a monumental edifice at which all the mothers work. Is this really a community? Not at all. It is a city in which the inhabitants have neighbours, not collaborators. Each mother kneads her pots of honey; each amasses a dowry for her offspring and nothing but a dowry for her offspring; each wears herself out for her family and only for her family. Oh, it would be a serious business if some one merely came and alighted on the brim of a cell that did not belong to her; the mistress of the house would give her to understand, by means of a sound drubbing, that manners such as those are not to be endured! She would have to skedaddle very quickly, unless she wanted a fight. The rights of property are sacred here.

Even the much more social Hive-bee is no exception to the rule of maternal egoism. To each hive one mother. If there be two, civil war breaks out and one of them perishes by the other's dagger or else quits the country, followed by a part of the swarm. Although virtually fit to lay eggs, the other Bees, to the number of some twenty thousand, renounce maternity and vow themselves to celibacy in order to bring up the prodigious

family of the one and only mother. Here,
communism reigns, under certain aspects; but,
for the immense majority, motherhood is
forthwith abolished.

Even so with the Wasps, the Ants, the
Termites[1] and the various social insects. Life
in common costs them dear. Thousands and
thousands remain incomplete and become the
humble auxiliaries of a few who are sexually
endowed. But, whenever maternity is the
general portion, individualism reappears, as
among the Mason-bees, notwithstanding their
show of communism.

The Pine Caterpillars are exempt from the
duty of preserving the race. They have no
sex, or rather are obscurely preparing one, as
undecided and rudimentary as all that is not
yet but must one day be. With the blossom-
ing of maternity, that flower of adult age,
individual property will not fail to appear,
attended by its rivalries. The insect now so
peaceable will, like the others, have its displays of selfish intolerance. The mothers
will isolate themselves, jealous of the double
pine-needle in which the cylinder of eggs is
to be fixed; the males, fluttering their wings,

[1] White Ants.—*Translator's Note.*

will challenge one another for the possession of the coveted bride. It is not a serious struggle among these easy-going ones, but still it presents a faint picture of those mortal affrays which the mating so often produces. Love rules the world by battle; it too is a hotbed of competition.

The caterpillar, being almost sexless, is indifferent to amorous instincts. This is the first condition for living pacifically in common. But it is not enough. The perfect concord of the community demands among all its members an equal division of strength and talent, of taste and capacity for work. This condition, which perhaps is the most important of all, is fulfilled preeminently. If there were hundreds, if there were thousands of them in the same nest, there would be no difference between any of them.

They are all the same size and equally strong; all wear the same dress; all possess the same gift for spinning; and all with equal zeal expend the contents of their silk-glands for the general welfare. No one idles, no one lounges along when there is work to be done. With no other stimulus than the satisfaction of doing their duty, every evening,

The Processionary: the Community

when the weather is favourable, they all spin
with equal industry and drain to the last drop
their reservoirs of silk, which have become
distended during the day. In their tribe there
is no question of skilled or unskilled, of strong
or weak, of abstemious or gluttonous; there
are neither hard-workers nor idlers, neither
savers nor spendthrifts. What one does the
others do, with a like zeal, no more and no
less well. It is a splendid world of equality
truly, but, alas, a world of caterpillars!

If it suited us to go to school to the Pine
Processionary, we should soon see the inanity
of our levelling and communistic theories.
Equality is a magnificent political catchword,
but little more. Where is it, this equality of
ours? In our social groups, could we find
as many as two persons exactly equal in
strength, health, intelligence, capacity for
work, foresight and all the other gifts which
are the great factors of prosperity? Where
should we find anything analogous to the exact
parity prevailing among caterpillars? Nowhere. Inequality is our law. And a good
thing, too.

A sound which is invariably the same, however often multiplied, does not constitute a

harmony.   We need dissimilarities, sounds loud and soft, deep and shrill; we need even discords which, by their harshness, throw into relief the sweetness of the chords.   In the same way, human societies are harmonious only with the aid of contraries.   If the dreams of our levellers could be realized, we should sink to the monotony of the caterpillar societies; art, science, progress and the lofty flights of the imagination would slumber indefinitely in the dead calm of mediocrity.

Besides, if this general levelling were effected, we should still be very far from communism.   To achieve that, we should have to do away with the family, as the caterpillars and Plato teach us; we should need abundance of food obtained without any effort.   So long as a mouthful of bread is difficult to acquire, demanding an industry and labour of which we are not all equally capable, so long as the family remains the sacred reason for our foresight, so long will the generous theory of all for each and each for all be absolutely impracticable.

And then should we gain by abolishing the struggle for the daily bread of ourselves and those dependent on us?   It is very doubtful.

The Processionary: the Community

We should be getting rid of this world's two great joys, work and the family, the only joys that give any value to life; we should be stifling exactly that which makes our greatness. And the result of this bestial sacrilege would be a community of human caterpillars. Thus does the Pine Processionary teach us by his example.

CHAPTER III

THE PINE PROCESSIONARY: THE PROCESSION

DROVER Dingdong's Sheep followed
the Ram which Panurge had maliciously
thrown overboard and leapt nimbly into the
sea, one after the other, "for you know," says
Rabelais, "it is the nature of the sheep always to follow the first, wheresoever it goes;
which makes Aristotle mark them for the
most silly and foolish animals in the world."[1]

The Pine Caterpillar is even more sheep-
like, not from foolishness, but from necessity:
where the first goes all the others go, in a
regular string, with not an empty space between them.

They proceed in single file, in a continuous
row, each touching with its head the rear of
the one in front of it. The complex twists
and turns described in his vagaries by the
caterpillar leading the van are scrupulously
described by all the others. No Greek *theoria*
winding its way to the Eleusinian festivals was

[1]Book IV., chap. viii.—*Translator's Note.*

The Processionary: the Procession

ever more orderly. Hence the name of
Processionary given to the gnawer of the
pine.

His character is complete when we add that
he is a rope-dancer all his life long: he walks
only on the tight-rope, a silken rail placed
in position as he advances. The caterpillar
who chances to be at the head of the procession dribbles his thread without ceasing and
fixes it on the path which his fickle preferences
cause him to take. The thread is so tiny that
the eye, though armed with a magnifying-
glass, suspects it rather than sees it.

But a second caterpillar steps on the slender
footboard and doubles it with his thread; a
third trebles it; and all the others, however
many there be, add the sticky spray from their
spinnerets, so much so that, when the procession has marched by, there remains, as a
record of its passing, a narrow white ribbon
whose dazzling whiteness shimmers in the
sun. Very much more sumptuous than ours,
their system of road-making consists in upholstering with silk instead of macadamizing.
We sprinkle our roads with broken stones and
level them by the pressure of a heavy steam-
roller; they lay over their paths a soft satin

rail, a work of general interest to which each contributes his thread.

What is the use of all this luxury? Could they not, like other caterpillars, walk about without these costly preparations? I see two reasons for their mode of progression. It is night when the Processionaries sally forth to browse upon the pine-leaves. They leave their nest, situated at the top of a bough, in profound darkness; they go down the denuded pole till they come to the nearest branch that has not yet been gnawed, a branch which becomes lower and lower by degrees as the consumers finish stripping the upper storeys; they climb up this untouched branch and spread over the green needles.

When they have had their suppers and begin to feel the keen night air, the next thing is to return to the shelter of the house. Measured in a straight line, the distance is not great, hardly an arm's length; but it cannot be covered in this way on foot. The caterpillars have to climb down from one crossing to the next, from the needle to the twig, from the twig to the branch, from the branch to the bough and from the bough, by a no less angular path, to go back home. It

The Processionary: the Procession

is useless to rely upon sight as a guide on this
long and erratic journey. The Processionary,
it is true, has five ocular specks on either side
of his head, but they are so infinitesimal, so
difficult to make out through the magnifying-
glass, that we cannot attribute to them any
great power of vision. Besides, what good
would those short-sighted lenses be in the
absence of light, in black darkness?

It is equally useless to think of the sense
of smell. Has the Processional any olfactory
powers or has he not? I do not know. Without giving a positive answer to the question,
I can at least declare that his sense of smell
is exceedingly dull and in no way suited to
help him find his way. This is proved, in
my experiments, by a number of hungry caterpillars that, after a long fast, pass close beside a pine-branch without betraying any
eagerness or showing a sign of stopping. It
is the sense of touch that tells them where
they are. So long as their lips do not chance
to light upon the pasture-land, not one of them
settles there, though he be ravenous. They
do not hasten to food which they have scented
from afar; they stop at a branch which they
encounter on their way.

The Life of the Caterpillar

Apart from sight and smell, what remains to guide them in returning to the nest? The ribbon spun on the road. In the Cretan labyrinth, Theseus would have been lost but for the clue of thread with which Ariadne supplied him. The spreading maze of the pine-needles is, especially at night, as inextricable a labyrinth as that constructed for Minos. The Processionary finds his way through it, without the possibility of a mistake, by the aid of his bit of silk. At the time for going home, each easily recovers either his own thread or one or other of the neighbouring threads, spread fanwise by the diverging herd; one by one the scattered tribe line up on the common ribbon, which started from the nest; and the sated caravan finds its way back to the manor with absolute certainty.

Longer expeditions are made in the day-time, even in winter, if the weather be fine. Our caterpillars then come down from the tree, venture on the ground, march in procession for a distance of thirty yards or so. The object of these sallies is not to look for food, for the native pine-tree is far from being exhausted: the shorn branches hardly count amid the vast leafage. Moreover, the caterpillars

observe complete abstinence till nightfall.
The trippers have no other object than a con-
stitutional, a pilgrimage to the outskirts to
see what these are like, possibly an inspection
of the locality where, later on, they mean to
bury themselves in the sand for their metamorphosis.

It goes without saying that, in these greater
evolutions, the guiding cord is not neglected.
It is now more necessary than ever. All con-
tribute to it from the produce of their spinnerets, as is the invariable rule whenever there
is a progression. Not one takes a step forward without fixing to the path the thread
hanging from his lip.

If the series forming the procession be at
all long, the ribbon is dilated sufficiently to
make it easy to find; nevertheless, on the
homeward journey, it is not picked up without some hesitation. For observe that the
caterpillars when on the march never turn
completely; to wheel round on their tight-rope
is a method utterly unknown to them. In
order therefore to regain the road already
covered, they have to describe a zig-zag whose
windings and extent are determined by the
leader's fancy. Hence come gropings and

roamings which are sometimes prolonged to
the point of causing the herd to spend the
night out of doors. It is not a serious matter. They collect into a motionless cluster.
To-morrow the search will start afresh and
will sooner or later be successful. Oftener
still the winding curve meets the guide-thread
at the first attempt. As soon as the first
caterpillar has the rail between his legs, all
hesitation ceases; and the band makes for the
nest with hurried steps.

The use of this silk-tapestried roadway is
evident from a second point of view. To protect himself against the severity of the winter which he has to face when working, the
Pine Caterpillar weaves himself a shelter in
which he spends his bad hours, his days of
enforced idleness. Alone, with none but the
meagre resources of his silk-glands, he would
find difficulty in protecting himself on the top
of a branch buffeted by the winds. A sub-
stantial dwelling, proof against snow, gales
and icy fogs, requires the cooperation of a
large number. Out of the individual's piled-
up atoms, the community obtains a spacious
and durable establishment.

The enterprise takes a long time to complete. Every evening, when the weather permits, the building has to be strengthened and enlarged. It is indispensable, therefore, that the corporation of workers should not be dissolved while the stormy season continues and the insects are still in the caterpillar stage. But, without special arrangements, each nocturnal expedition at grazing-time would be a cause of separation. At that moment of appetite for food there is a return to individualism. The caterpillars become more or less scattered, settling singly on the branches around; each browses his pine-needle separately. How are they to find one another afterwards and become a community again?

The several threads left on the road make this easy. With that guide, every caterpillar, however far he may be, comes back to his companions without ever missing the way. They come hurrying from a host of twigs, from here, from there, from above, from below; and soon the scattered legion reforms into a group. The silk thread is something more than a road-making expedient: it is the social bond, the system that keeps the members of the community indissolubly united.

At the head of every procession, long or

The Life of the Caterpillar

short, goes a first caterpillar whom I will call
the leader of the march or file, though the
word leader, which I use for want of a better, is a little out of place here. Nothing, in
fact, distinguishes this caterpillar from the
others: it just depends upon the order in
which they happen to line up; and mere chance
brings him to the front. Among the Processionaries, every captain is an officer of fortune. The actual leader leads; presently he
will be a subaltern, if the file should break up
in consequence of some accident and be
formed anew in a different order.

His temporary functions give him an attitude of his own. While the others follow
passively in a close file, he, the captain, tosses
himself about and with an abrupt movement
flings the front of his body hither and thither.
As he marches ahead he seems to be seeking
his way. Does he in point of fact explore the
country? Does he choose the most practicable
places? Or are his hesitations merely the result of the absence of a guiding thread on
ground that has not yet been covered? His
subordinates follow very placidly, reassured
by the cord which they hold between their
legs; he, deprived of that support, is uneasy.

The Processionary: the Procession

Why cannot I read what passes under his black, shiny skull, so like a drop of tar? To judge by actions, there is here a small dose of discernment which is able, after experimenting, to recognize excessive roughnesses,. over-slippery surfaces, dusty places that offer no resistance and, above all, the threads left by other excursionists. This is all or nearly 'all that my long acquaintance with the Processionaries has taught me as to their mentality. Poor brains, indeed; poor creatures, whose commonwealth has its safety hanging upon a thread!

The processions vary greatly in length. The finest that I have seen manœuvring on the ground measured twelve or thirteen yards and numbered about three hundred caterpillars, drawn up with absolute precision in a wavy line. But, if there were only two in a row, the order would still be perfect: the second touches and follows the first.

By February I have processions of all lengths in the greenhouse What tricks can I play upon them? I see only two: to do away with the leader; and to cut the thread.

The suppression of the leader of the file produces nothing striking. If the thing is

67

The Life of the Caterpillar

done without creating a disturbance, the procession does not alter its ways at all. The second caterpillar, promoted to captain, knows the duties of his rank off-hand: he selects and leads, or rather he hesitates and gropes.

The breaking of the silk ribbon is not very important either. I remove a caterpillar from the middle of the file. With my scissors, so as not to cause a commotion in the ranks, I cut the piece of ribbon on which he stood and clear away every thread of it. As a result of this breach, the procession acquires two marching leaders, each independent of the other. It may be that the one in the rear joins the file ahead of him, from which he is separated by but a slender interval; in that case, things return to their original condition. More frequently, the two parts do not become reunited. In that case, we have two distinct processions, each of which wanders where it pleases and diverges from the other. Nevertheless, both will be able to return to the nest by discovering sooner or later, in the course of their peregrinations, the ribbon on the other side of the break.

These two experiments are only moderately

The Processionary: the Procession

interesting. I have thought out another, one more fertile in possibilities. I propose to make the caterpillars describe a close circuit, after the ribbons running from it and liable to bring about a change of direction have been destroyed. The locomotive engine pursues its invariable course so long as it is not shunted on to a branch-line. If the Processionaries find the silken rail always clear in front of them, with no switches anywhere, will they continue on the same track, will they persist in following a road that never comes to an end? What we have to do is to produce this circuit, which is unknown under ordinary conditions, by artificial means.

The first idea that suggests itself is to seize with the forceps the silk ribbon at the back of the train, to bend it without shaking it and to bring the end of it ahead of the file. If the caterpillar marching in the van steps upon it, the thing is done: the others will follow him faithfully. The operation is very simple in theory but very difficult in practice and produces no useful results. The ribbon, which is extremely slight, breaks under the weight of the grains of sand that stick to it and are lifted with it. If it does not break, the caterpill..rs at the back, however delicately we may go to work, feel a disturbance which makes them curl up or even let go.

There is a yet greater difficulty: the leader refuses the ribbon laid before him; the cut end makes him distrustful. Failing to see the regular, uninterrupted road, he slants off to the right or left, he escapes at a tangent. If I try to interfere and to bring him back to the path of my choosing, he persists in his refusal, shrivels up, does not budge; and soon the whole procession is in confusion. We will not insist: the method is a poor one, very wasteful of effort for at best a problematical success.

We ought to interfere as little as possible and obtain a natural closed circuit. Can it be done? Yes. It lies in our power, without the least meddling, to see a procession march along a perfect circular track. I owe this result, which is eminently deserving of our attention, to pure chance.

On the shelf with the layer of sand in which the nests are planted stand some big palm-vases measuring nearly a yard and a half in circumference at the top. The caterpillars often scale the sides and climb up to the

The Processionary: the Procession

moulding which forms a cornice around the opening. This place suits them for their processions, perhaps because of the absolute firmness of the surface, where there is no fear of landslides, as on the loose, sandy soil below; and also, perhaps, because of the horizontal position, which is favorable to repose after the fatigue of the ascent. It provides me with a circular track all ready-made. I have nothing to do but wait for an occasion propitious to my plans. This occasion is not long in coming.

On the 30th of January, 1896, a little before twelve o'clock in the day, I discover a numerous troop making their way up and gradually reaching the popular cornice. Slowly, in single file, the caterpillars climb the great vase, mount the ledge and advance in regular procession, while others are constantly arriving and continuing the series. I wait for the string to close up, that is to say, for the leader, who keeps following the circular moulding, to return to the point from which he started. My object is achieved in a quarter of an hour. The closed circuit is realized magnificently, in something very nearly approaching a circle.

The Life of the Caterpillar

The next thing is to get rid of the rest of the ascending column, which would disturb the fine order of the procession by an excess of newcomers; it is also important that we should do away with all the silken paths, both new and old, that can put the cornice into communication with the ground. With a thick hair-pencil I sweep away the surplus climbers; with a big brush, one that leaves no smell behind it—for this might afterwards prove confusing—I carefully rub down the vase and get rid of every thread which the caterpillars have laid on the march. When these preparations are finished, a curious sight awaits us.

In the uninterrupted circular procession there is no longer a leader. Each caterpillar is preceded by another on whose heels he follows, guided by the silk track, the work of the whole party; he again has a companion close behind him, following him in the same orderly way. And this is repeated without variation throughout the length of the chain. None commands, or rather none modifies the trail according to his fancy; all obey, trusting in the guide who ought normally to lead the

The Processionary: the Procession

march and who in reality has been abolished by my trickery.

From the first circuit of the edge of the tub the rail of silk has been laid in position and is soon turned into a narrow ribbon by the procession, which never ceases dribbling its thread as it goes. The rail is simply doubled and has no branches anywhere, for my brush has destroyed them all. What will the caterpillars do on this deceptive, closed path? Will they walk endlessly round and round until their strength gives out entirely?

The old schoolmen were fond of quoting Buridan's[1] Ass, that famous Donkey who, when placed between two bundles of hay, starved to death because he was unable to decide in favour of either by breaking the equilibrium between two equal but opposite attractions. They slandered the worthy animal. The Ass, who is no more foolish than any one else, would reply to the logical snare by feasting off both bundles. Will my cater-

[1] Jean Buridan (*circa* 1300-*circa* 1360), a famous scholastic doctor, who was several times rector of the university of Paris and subsequently founded the university of Vienna. He forms the subject of many legends, including that of the argument known by his name, of which no trace is to be found in any of his works.—*Translator's Note.*

The Life of the Caterpillar

pillars show a little of his mother wit? Will they, after many attempts, be able to break the equilibrium of their closed circuit, which keeps them on a road without a turning? Will they make up their minds to swerve to this side or that, which is the only method of reaching their bundle of hay, the green branch yonder, quite near, not two feet off?

I thought that they would and I was wrong. I said to myself:

"The procession will go on turning for some time, for an hour, two hours perhaps; then the caterpillars will perceive their mistake. They will abandon the deceptive road and make their descent somewhere or other."

That they should remain up there, hard pressed by hunger and the lack of cover, when nothing prevented them from going away, seemed to me inconceivable imbecility. Facts, however, forced me to accept the incredible. Let us describe them in detail.

The circular procession begins, as I have said, on the 30th of January, about midday, in splendid weather. The caterpillars march at an even pace, each touching the stern of the one in front of him. The unbroken chain eliminates the leader with his changes of direc-

The Processionary: the Procession

tion; and all follow mechanically, as faithful to their circle as are the hands of a watch. The headless file has no liberty left, no will; it has become mere clock-work. And this continues for hours and hours. My success goes far beyond my wildest suspicions. I stand amazed at it, or rather I am stupefied.

Meanwhile, the multiplied circuits change the original rail into a superb ribbon a twelfth of an inch broad. I can easily see it glittering on the red ground of the pot. The day is drawing to a close and no alteration has yet taken place in the position of the trail. A striking proof confirms this.

The trajectory is not a plane curve, but one which, at a certain point, deviates and goes down a little way to the lower surface of the cornice, returning to the top some eight inches farther. I marked these two points of deviation in pencil on the vase at the outset. Well, all that afternoon and, more conclusive still, on the following days, right to the end of this mad dance, I see the string of caterpillars dip under the ledge at the first point and come to the top again at the second. Once the first thread is laid, the road to be pursued is permanently established.

The Life of the Caterpillar

If the road does not vary, the speed does. I measure nine centimetres[1] a minute as the average distance covered. But there are more or less lengthy halts; the pace slackens at times, especially when the temperature falls. At ten o'clock in the evening the walk is little more than a lazy swaying of the body. I foresee an early halt, in consequence of the cold, of fatigue and doubtless also of hunger.

Grazing-time has arrived. The caterpillars have come crowding from all the nests in the greenhouse to browse upon the pine-branches planted by myself beside the silken purses. Those in the garden do the same, for the temperature is mild. The others, lined up along the earthenware cornice, would gladly take part in the feast; they are bound to have an appetite after a ten hours' walk. The branch stands green and tempting not a hand's breadth away. To reach it they need but go down; and the poor wretches, foolish slaves of their ribbon that they are, cannot make up their minds to do so. I leave the famished ones at half-past ten, persuaded that they will take counsel with their pillow and

[1] 3½ inches.—*Translator's Note.*

76

that on the morrow things will have resumed their ordinary course.

I was wrong. I was expecting too much of them when I accorded them that faint gleam of intelligence which the tribulations of a distressful stomach ought, one would think, to have aroused. I visit them at dawn. They are lined up as on the day before, but motionless. When the air grows a little warmer, they shake off their torpor, revive and start walking again. The circular procession begins anew, like that which I have already seen. There is nothing more and nothing less to be noted in their machine-like obstinacy.

This time it is a bitter night. A cold snap has supervened, was indeed foretold in the evening by the garden caterpillars, who refused to come out despite appearances which to my duller senses seemed to promise a continuation of the fine weather. At daybreak the rosemary-walks are all asparkle with rime and for the second time this year there is a sharp frost. The large pond in the garden is frozen over. What can the caterpillars in the conservatory be doing? Let us go and see.

All are ensconced in their nests, except the

77

The Life of the Caterpillar

stubborn processionists on the edge of the vase, who, deprived of shelter as they are, seem to have spent a very bad night. I find them clustered in two heaps, without any attempt at order. They have suffered less from the cold, thus huddled together.

'Tis an ill wind that blows nobody any good. The severity of the night has caused the ring to break into two segments which will, perhaps, afford a chance of safety. Each group, as it revives and resumes its walk, will presently be headed by a leader who, not being obliged to follow a caterpillar in front of him, will possess some liberty of movement and perhaps be able to make the procession swerve to one side. Remember that, in the ordinary processions, the caterpillar walking ahead acts as a scout. While the others, if nothing occurs to create excitement, keep to their ranks, he attends to his duties as a leader and is continually turning his head to this side and that, investigating, seeking, groping, making his choice. And things happen as he decides: the band follows him faithfully. Remember also that, even on a road which has already been travelled and beribboned, the guiding caterpillar continues to explore.

The Processionary: the Procession

There is reason to believe that the Processionaries who have lost their way on the ledge will find a chance of safety here. Let us watch them. On recovering from their torpor, the two groups line up by degrees into two distinct files. There are therefore two leaders, free to go where they please, independent of each other. Will they succeed in leaving the enchanted circle? At the sight of their large black heads swaying anxiously from side to side, I am inclined to think so for a moment. But I am soon undeceived. As the ranks fill out, the two sections of the chain meet and the circle is reconstituted. The momentary leaders once more become simple subordinates; and again the caterpillars march round and round all day.

For the second time in succession, the night, which is very calm and magnificently starry, brings a hard frost. In the morning the Processionaries on the tub, the only ones who have camped out unsheltered, are gathered into a heap which largely overflows both sides of the fatal ribbon. I am present at the awakening of the numbed ones. The first to take the road is, as luck will have it, outside

the track.   Hesitatingly he ventures into unknown ground.   He reaches the top of the
rim and descends upon the other side on the
earth in the vase.   He is followed by six
others, no more.   Perhaps the rest of the
troop, who have not fully recovered from
their nocturnal torpor, are to lazy to bestir
themselves.

The result of this brief delay is a return
to the old track.   The caterpillars embark on
the silken trail and the circular march is resumed, this time in the form of a ring with
a gap in it.   There is no attempt, however, to
strike a new course on the part of the guide
whom this gap has placed at the head.   A
chance of stepping outside the magic circle has
presented itself at last; and he does not know
how to avail himself of it.

As for the caterpillars who have made their
way to the inside of the vase, their lot is hardly improved.   They climb to the top of the
palm, starving and seeking for food.   Finding
nothing to eat that suits them, they retrace
their steps by following the thread which they
have left on the way, climb the ledge of the
pot, strike the procession again and, without
further anxiety, slip back into the ranks.

The Processionary: the Procession

Once more the ring is complete, once more the circle turns and turns.

Then when will the deliverance come? There is a legend that tells of poor souls dragged along in an endless round until the hellish charm is broken by a drop of holy water. What drop will good fortune sprinkle on my Processionaries to dissolve their circle and bring them back to the nest? I see only two means of conjuring the spell and obtaining a release from the circuit. These two means are two painful ordeals. A strange linking of cause and effect: from sorrow and wretchedness good is to come.

And, first, shrivelling as the result of cold. The caterpillars gather together without any order, heap themselves some on the path, some, more numerous these, outside it. Among the latter there may be, sooner or later, some revolutionary who, scorning the beaten track, will trace out a new road and lead the troop back home. We have just seen an instance of it. Seven penetrated to the interior of the vase and climbed the palm. True, it was an attempt with no result, but still an attempt. For complete success, all that need be done would have been to take the opposite slope. An even chance is a great thing. Another time we shall be more successful.

In the second place, the exhaustion due to fatigue and hunger. A lame one stops, unable to go farther. In front of the defaulter the procession still continues to wend its way for a short time. The ranks close up and an empty space appears. On coming to himself and resuming the march, the caterpillar who has caused the breach becomes a leader, having nothing before him. The least desire for emancipation is all that he wants to make him launch the band into a new path which perhaps will be the saving path.

In short, when the Processionaries' train is in difficulties, what it needs, unlike ours, is to run off the rails. The side-tracking is left to the caprice of a leader who alone is capable of turning to the right or left; and this leader is absolutely non-existent so long as the ring remains unbroken. Lastly, the breaking of the circle, the one stroke of luck, is the result of a chaotic halt, caused principally by excess of fatigue or cold.

The liberating accident, especially that of fatigue, occurs fairly often. In the course of

The Processionary: the Procession

the same day, the moving circumference is cut up several times into two or three sections; but continuity soon returns and no change takes place. Things go on just the same. The bold innovator who is to save the situation has not yet had his inspiration.

There is nothing new on the fourth day, after an icy night like the previous one; nothing to tell except the following detail. Yesterday I did not remove the trace left by the few caterpillars who made their way to the inside of the vase. This trace, together with a junction connecting it with the circular road, is discovered in the course of the morning. Half the troop takes advantage of it to visit the earth in the pot and climb the palm; the other half remains on the ledge and continues to walk along the old rail. In the afternoon the band of emigrants rejoins the others, the circuit is completed and things return to their original condition.

We come to the fifth day. The night frost becomes more intense, without however as yet reaching the greenhouse. It is followed by bright sunshine in a calm and limpid sky. As soon as the sun's rays have warmed the panes a little, the caterpillars, lying in

heaps, wake up and resume their evolutions
on the ledge of the vase. This time the fine
order of the beginning is disturbed and a certain disorder becomes manifest, apparently an
omen of deliverance near at hand. The
scouting-path inside the vase, which was upholstered in silk yesterday and the day before,
is to-day followed to its origin on the rim
by a part of the band and is then abandoned
after a short loop. The other caterpillars
follow the usual ribbon. The result of this
bifurcation is two almost equal files, walking
along the ledge in the same direction, at a
short distance from each other, sometimes
meeting, separating farther on, in every case
with some lack of order.

Weariness increases the confusion. The
crippled, who refuse to go on, are many.
Breaches increase; files are split up into sections each of which has its leader, who pokes
the front of his body this way and that to
explore the ground. Everything seems to
point to the disintegration which will bring
safety. My hopes are once more disappointed. Before the night the single file is
reconstituted and the invincible gyration resumed.

The Processionary: the Procession

Heat comes, just as suddenly as the cold did. To-day, the 4th of February, is a beautiful, mild day. The greenhouse is full of life. Numerous festoons of caterpillars, issuing from the nests, meander along the sand on the shelf. Above them, at every moment, the ring on the ledge of the vase breaks up and comes together again. For the first time I see daring leaders who, drunk with heat, standing only on their hinder prolegs at the extreme edge of the earthenware rim, fling themselves forward into space, twisting about, sounding the depths. The endeavour is frequently repeated, while the whole troop stops. The caterpillars' heads give sudden jerks; their bodies wriggle.

One of the pioneers decides to take the plunge. He slips under the ledge. Four follow him. The others, still confiding in the perfidious silken path, dare not copy him and continue to go along the old road.

The short string detached from the general chain gropes about a great deal, hesitates long on the side of the vase; it goes half-way down, then climbs up again slantwise, rejoins and takes its place in the procession. This time the attempt has failed, though at the foot of the vase, not nine inches away, there lay a bunch of pine-needles which I had placed there with the object of enticing the hungry ones. Smell and sight told them nothing. Near as they were to the goal, they went up again.

No matter, the endeavour has its uses. Threads were laid on the way and will serve as a lure to further enterprise. The road of deliverance has its first landmarks. And two days later, on the eighth day of the experiment, the caterpillars—now singly, anon in small groups, then again in strings of some length—come down from the ledge by following the staked-out path. At sunset the last of the laggards is back in the nest.

Now for a little arithmetic. For seven times twenty-four hours the caterpillars have remained on the ledge of the vase. To make an ample allowance for stops due to the weariness of this one or that and above all for the rest taken during the colder hours of the night, we will deduct one-half of the time. This leaves eighty-four hours' walking. The average pace is nine centimetres[1] a minute.

[1] 3½ inches.—*Translator's Note.*

The Processionary: the Proeession

The aggregate distance covered, therefore, is
453 metres, a good deal more than a quarter
of a mile, which is a great walk for these
little crawlers. The circumference of the vase,
the perimeter of the track, is exactly 1 m. 35.[1]
Therefore the circle covered, always in the
same direction and always without result,
was described three hundred and thirty-five
times.

These figures surprise me, though I am
already familiar with the abysmal stupidity
of insects as a class whenever the least accident occurs. I feel inclined to ask myself
whether the Processionaries were not kept up
there so long by the difficulties and dangers
of the descent rather than by the lack of any
gleam of intelligence in their benighted minds.
The facts, however, reply that the descent is
as easy as the ascent.

The caterpillar has a very supple back, well
adapted for twisting round projections or slipping underneath. He can walk with the same
ease vertically or horizontally, with his back
down or up. Besides, he never moves forward until he has fixed his thread to the
ground. With this support to his feet, he

[1] 4 feet 5 inches.—*Translator's Note.*

has no falls to fear, no matter what his position.

I had a proof of this before my eyes during a whole week. As I have already said, the track, instead of keeping on one level, bends twice, dips at a certain point under the ledge of the vase and reappears at the top a little farther on. At one part of the circuit, therefore, the procession walks on the lower surface of the rim; and this inverted position implies so little discomfort or danger that it is renewed at each turn for all the caterpillars from first to last.

It is out of the question then to suggest the dread of a false step on the edge of the rim which is so nimbly turned at each point of inflexion. The caterpillars in distress, starved, shelterless, chilled with cold at night, cling obstinately to the silk ribbon covered hundreds of times, because they lack the rudimentary glimmers of reason which would advice them to abandon it.

Experience and reflection are not in their province. The ordeal of a five hundred yards' march and three to four hundred turns teach them nothing; and it takes casual circumstances to bring them back to the nest. They would perish on their insidious ribbon if the disorder of the nocturnal encampments and the halts due to fatigue did not cast a few threads outside the circular path. Some three or four move along these trails, laid without an object, stray a little way and, thanks to their wanderings, prepare the descent, which is at last accomplished in short strings favoured by chance.

The school most highly honoured to-day is very anxious to find the origin of reason in the dregs of the animal kingdom. Let me call its attention to the Pine Processionary.

CHAPTER IV

IN JANUARY a second moult occurs, leaving the caterpillar less fair to the eye, while at the same time endowing him with some very peculiar organs. When the moment has come to shed their skins, the Processionaries cluster higgledy-piggledy on the dome of the nest and there, if the weather be mild, remain motionless day and night. It would seem as though the fact of their contact, of their mutual discomfort, while thus heaped together, furnishes a resistance, a fulcrum, which favours the process of excoriation.

After this second moult, the hairs on the middle of the back are of a dull reddish colour, which is made paler still by the interposition of numerous long white hairs. But this faded costume is accompanied by the singular organs which attracted the attention of Réaumur, who was greatly perplexed as to their function. In the place originally occupied by the scarlet mosaic, eight segments of the caterpillar are now cleft by a broad transversal gash, a sort of thick-lipped mouth, which opens and gapes wide at the caterpillar's will, or closes without leaving a visible trace.

From each of these expanding mouths rises a tumour with a fine, colourless skin, as though the creature were exposing its tender inside and inflating it, for the appearance is almost that which would be presented by the viscera protruding through skin incised by the scalpel. Two large dark-brown dots occupy the front face of the protuberance. At the back are two short, flat tufts of russet bristles, which in the sunlight shine with a rich brilliancy. All around is a radiating border of long white hairs, spread almost flat.

This protuberance is extremely sensitive. At the slightest irritation it goes in again and disappears under the dark integument. In its place opens an oval crater, a sort of huge stoma, which swiftly brings its lips together, closes and entirely disappears. The long white hairs that form a moustache and imperial around this mouth follow the movements of the contracting lips. After first radiating from a centre and lying flat, these hairs rise like levelled wheat which the wind

The Life of the Caterpillar

has caught from beneath and meet to form a transversal crest, perpendicular to the creature's back.

This hairy erection produces a sudden modification in the caterpillar's aspect. The red shiny bristles have disappeared, buried under the dark skin; the white hairs, now standing on end, form a hirsute mane; an ashy tinge has crept into the general colour of the costume.

When calm is restored, as soon happens, the slits open and yawn afresh; the sensitive protuberances emerge, quick to disappear once more should any cause for alarm occur. These alternate expansions and contractions are rapidly repeated. I provoke them at will in various ways. A slight puff of tobacco-smoke immediately causes the stomata to yawn and the protuberances to emerge. One would think that the insect was putting itself on its guard and displaying some special apparatus of information. Before long the protuberances go in again. A second puff of smoke brings them out once more. But, if the smoke is too abundant, too acrid, the caterpillar wriggles and writhes without opening his apparatus.

The Processionary: Meteorology

Or else I touch one or other of these uncovered protuberances, very delicately, with
a bit of straw. The pimple affected immediately contracts, draws into itself, like the
horns of the Snail, and is replaced by a gaping mouth, which in its turn closes. Usually,
but not always, the segment excited by the
contact of my straw is imitated by the others,
both front and back, which close their apparatus one by one.

When undisturbed and in repose, the caterpillar generally has his dorsal slits expanded;
in moving, he sometimes opens and sometimes
closes them. In either case expansion and
contraction are frequently repeated. Constantly coming together and retreating under
the skin, the lips of the mouth-like opening
therefore end by losing their brittle moustaches of russet hairs, which break off. In this
way a sort of dust collects at the bottom of
the crater, a dust formed of broken hairs,
which, thanks to their barbs, soon collect into
little tufts. When the slit expands rather suddenly, the central projection shoots out on
the insect's sides its load of hairy remnants,
which the least breath blows into a cloud of
golden atoms highly disagreeable to the ob-

server. I shall have something to say presently of the itch to which he is at such times exposed.

Are these peculiar stomata designed merely to collect the adjoining bristles and to grind them to powder? Are these fine-skinned papillæ, which inflate and ascend from the depths of their hiding-place, intended to get rid of the accumulation of broken hairs? Or is it the sole function of this peculiar apparatus to prepare, at the expense of the caterpillar's fleece, an irritant dust which shall act as a means of defence? Nothing tells us so.

Certainly the caterpillar is not armed against the enquirer who from time to time takes it into his head to come and examine him through a magnifying-glass. It is even very doubtful whether he troubles at all about those passionate caterpillar-lovers, *Calosoma sycophanta*[1] among insects and the Cuckoo among birds. Those who consume such fare have a stomach expressly fashioned for the purpose, a stomach that laughs at blistering hairs and possibly finds an appetizing stimulant in their sting. No, I do not see the motives that prompted the Processionary to

[1] A large carnivorous Beetle.—*Translator's Note.*

cleave his back with so many slits, if he merely strips himself of his hair to throw an irritating dust in our eyes. There must certainly be something else in question.

Réaumur mentions these openings, of which he made a brief study. He calls them stigmata and is inclined to take them for exceptional breathing-holes. That they are not, O my master; no insect contrives air-holes on its back! Moreover, the magnifying-glass reveals no channel of communication with the interior. Respiration plays no part here; the solution of the enigma must lie elsewhere.

The protuberances that rise from those expanded cavities are formed of a soft, pale, hairless membrane, which gives the impression of a visceral hernia, as though the caterpillar were wounded and exposing its delicate entrails to the air. The sensitiveness just here is great. The lightest touch with the point of a hair-pencil causes the immediate indrawing of the protuberances and the closing of the containing lips.

The touch of a solid object even is not essential. I pick up a tiny drop of water on the point of a pin and, without shaking it off, present this drop to the sensitive projection.

The Life of the Caterpillar

At the moment when contact occurs the apparatus contracts and closes up. The recoil of the Snail's horns, withdrawing the visual and olfactory organs into their sheaths, is no prompter.

Everything seems to prove that these optional tumours, appearing and disappearing at the caterpillar's will, are instruments of sensorial perception. The caterpillar exposes them to obtain information; he shelters them under his skin to preserve their delicate functions. Now what is it that they perceive? This is a difficult question, in which the habits of the Processionary alone can afford us a little guidance.

During the whole winter, the Pine Caterpillars are active only at night. In the daytime, when the weather is fine, they readily repair to the dome of the nest and there remain motionless, gathered into heaps. It is the hour of the open-air siesta, under the pale December and January sun. As yet none leaves the home. It is quite late in the evening, towards nine o'clock, when they set out, marching in an irregular procession, to browse on the leaves of the branches hard by. Their grazing is a protracted affair. The flock returns late, some time after midnight, when the temperature falls too low.

Secondly, it is in the heart of winter, during the roughest months, that the Processionary displays his full activity. Indefatigably at this time of year he spins, adding each night a new web to his silken tent; at this time, whenever the weather permits, he ventures abroad on the neighbouring boughs to feed, to grow and to renew his skein of silk.

By a very remarkable exception, the harsh season marked by inactivity and lethargic repose in other insects is for him the season of bustle and labour, on condition, of course, that the inclemencies of the weather do not exceed certain limits. If the north wind blow too violently, so that it is like to sweep the flock away; if the cold be too piercing, so that there is a risk of freezing to death; if it snow, or rain, or if the mist thicken into an icy drizzle, the caterpillars prudently stay at home, sheltering under their weatherproof tent.

It would be convenient to some extent to foresee these inclemencies. The caterpillar dreads them. A drop of rain sets him in a flutter; a snowflake exasperates him. To

The Life of the Caterpillar

start for the grazing-grounds at dark of night, in uncertain weather, would be dangerous, for the procession goes some distance and travels slowly. The flock would fare ill before regaining shelter did any sudden atmospheric trouble supervene, an event of some frequency in the bad season of the year. So that he may be informed in this particular during his nocturnal winter rambles, can the Pine Caterpillar be endowed with some sort of meteorological aptitudes? Let us describe how the suspicion occurred to me.

Divulged I know not how, my rearing of caterpillars under glass acquired a certain renown. It was talked about in the village. The forest-ranger, a sworn enemy to destructive insects, wanted to see the grazing of the famous caterpillars, of whom he had retained a too poignant memory ever since the day when he gathered and destroyed their nests in a pine-wood under his charge. It was arranged that he should call the same evening.

He arrives at the appointed hour, accompanied by a friend. For a moment we sit and chat in front of the fire; then, when the clock strikes nine, the lantern is lit and we

The Processionary: Meteorology

all three enter the greenhouse. The visitors
are eager for the spectacle of which they have
heard such wonderful things, while I am certain of satisfying their curiosity.

But, but . . . what is this? Not a caterpillar on the nests, not one on the fresh ration
of branches! Last night and on the previous
nights they came out in countless numbers;
to-night not one reveals himself. Can it be
that they are merely late in going to dinner?
Can their habitual punctuality be at fault because appetite has not yet arrived? We must
be patient. . . . Ten o'clock. Nothing.
Eleven. Still nothing. Midnight was at hand
when we abandoned our watch, convinced that
it would be vain to prolong the sitting. You
can imagine what an abject fool I looked
at having thus to send my guests away.

Next day I thought that I dimly perceived
the explanation of this disappointment. It
rained in the night and again in the morning.
Snow, not the earliest of the year, but so
far the most abundant, whitened the brow of
the Ventoux.[1] Had the caterpillars, more

[1]The highest mountain in the neighbourhood of
Sérignan. Cf. *The Hunting Wasps,* by J. Henri Fabre,
translated by Alexander Teixeira de Mattos: chap. xl.
—*Translator's Note.*

sensitive than any of us to atmospheric changes, refused to venture forth because they anticipated what was about to happen? Had they foreseen the rain and the snow, which nothing seemed to announce, at all events to us? After all, why not? Let us continue to observe them and we shall see whether the coincidence is fortuitous or not.

On this memorable day, therefore, the 13th of December, 1895, I institute the caterpillars' meteorological observatory. I have at my disposal absolutely none of the apparatus dear to science, not even a modest thermometer, for my unlucky star continues in the ascendant, proving as unkind to-day as when I learnt chemistry with pipe-bowls for crucibles and bottles that once contained sweets for retorts. I confine myself to visiting nightly the Processionaries in the greenhouse and those in the garden. It is a hard task, especially as I have to go to the far end of the enclosure, often in weather when one would not turn a Dog out of doors. I set down the acts of the caterpillars, whether they come out or stay at home; I note the state of the sky during the day and at the moment of my evening examination.

The Processionary : Meteorology

To this list I add the meteorological chart
of Europe which the *Temps* publishes daily.
If I want more precise data, I request the
Normal School at Avignon to send me, on
occasions of violent disturbances, the barome-
trical records of its observatory. These are
the only documents at my disposal.

Before we come to the results obtained, let
me once more repeat that my caterpillars'
meteorological institute has two stations: one
in the greenhouse and one in the open air,
on the pines in the enclosure. The first, protected against the wind and rain, is that which
I prefer: it provides more regular and more
continuous information. In fact, the open-
air caterpillars often enough refuse to come
out, even though the general conditions be
favourable. It is enough to keep them at
home if there be too strong a wind shaking
the boughs, or even a little moisture dripping
on the web of the nests. Saved from these
two perils, the greenhouse caterpillars have
only to consider atmospheric incidents of a
higher order. The small variations escape
them; the great alone make an impression on
them: a most useful point for the observer
and going a long way towards solving the

problem for him. The colonies under glass, therefore, provide most of the material for my notes; the colonies in the open air add their testimony, which is not always quite clear.

Now what did they tell me, those greenhouse caterpillars who, on the 13th of December, refused to show themselves to my guest, the forest-ranger? The rain that was to fall that night could hardly have alarmed them: they were so well sheltered. The snow about to whiten Mont Ventoux was nothing to them: it was so far away. Moreover, it was neither snowing yet nor raining. Some extraordinary atmospheric event, profound and of vast extent, must have been occurring. The charts in the *Temps* and the bulletin of the Normal School told me as much.

A cyclonic disturbance, coming from the British Isles, was passing over our district; an atmospheric depression the like of which the season had not as yet known, had spread in our direction, reaching us on the 13th and persisting, in a more or less accentuated form, until the 22nd. At Avignon the barometer suddenly fell half an inch, to 29.1 in., on the 13th and lower still, to 29 in., on the 19th.

The Processionary: Meteorology

During this period of ten days, the garden caterpillars made no sortie on the pine-trees. True, the weather was changeable. There were a few showers of fine rain and some violent gusts of the mistral; but more frequently there were days and nights when the sky was superb and the temperature moderate. The prudent anchorites would not allow themselves to be caught. The low pressure peristed, menacing them; and so they stopped at home.

In the greenhouse things happen rather differently. Sorties take place, but the staying-in days are still more numerous. It looks as though the caterpillars, alarmed at first by the unexpected things happening overhead, had reassured themselves and resumed work, feeling nothing, in their shelter, of what they would have suffered out of doors—rain, snow and furious mistral blasts—and had then suspended their work again when the threats of bad weather increased.

There is, indeed, a fairly accurate agreement between the oscillations of the barometer and the decisions of the herd. When the column of mercury rises a little, they come out; when it falls they remain at home. Thus on the 19th, the night of the lowest pressure, 29 in., not a caterpillar ventures outside.

As the wind and rain can have no effect on my colonies under glass, one is led to suppose that atmospheric pressure, with its physiological results, so difficult to define, is here the principal factor. As for the temperature, within moderate limits there is no need to discuss it. The Processionaries have a robust constitution, as behoves spinners who work in the open air in midwinter. However piercing the cold, so long as it does not freeze, when the hour comes for working or feeding they spin on the surface of the nest or browse on the neighbouring branches.

Another example. According to the meteorological chart in the *Temps,* a depression whose centre is near the Iles Sanguinaires, at the entrance of the Gulf of Ajaccio, reaches my neighbourhood, with a minimum of 29.2 in., on the 9th of January. A tempestuous wind gets up. For the first time this year there is a respectable frost. The ice on the large pond in the garden is two or three inches thick. This wild weather lasts for five days. Of course, the garden caterpillars do not sally forth on the pine-trees while these are battered by such a gale.

The remarkable part of the business is that the greenhouse caterpillars do not venture out of their nests either. And yet for them there are no boughs dangerously shaken, no cold piercing beyond endurance, for it is not freezing under the glass. What keeps them in can be only the passage of that wave of depression. On the 15th the storm ceases; and the barometer remains between 29.6 and 30 in. for the rest of the month and a good part of February. During this long period there are magnificent sorties every evening, especially in the greenhouse.

On the 23rd and 24th of February, suddenly the Processionaries stop at home again, for no apparent reason. Of the six nests under cover, only two have a few rare caterpillars out on the pine-branches, while previously, in the case of all six, I used every night to see the leaves bending under the weight of an innumerable multitude. Warned by this forecast, I enter in my notes:

"Some deep depression is about to reach us."

And I have guessed right. Two days later,

sure enough, the meteorological record of the *Temps* gives me the following information: a minimum of 29.2 in., coming from the Bay of Biscay on the 22nd, reaches Algeria on the 23rd and spreads over the Provence coast on the 24th. There is a heavy snowfall at Marseilles on the 25th.

"The ships," I read in my paper, "present a curious spectacle, with their yards and rigging white. That is how the people of Marseilles, little used to such sights, picture Spitzbergen and the North Pole."

Here certainly is the gale which my caterpillars foresaw when they refused to go out last night and the night before; here is the centre of disturbance which revealed itself at Sérignan by a violent and icy north wind on the 25th and the following days. Again I perceive that the greenhouse caterpillars are alarmed only at the approach of the wave of atmospheric disturbance. Once the first uneasiness caused by the depression had abated, they came out again, on the 25th and the following days, in the midst of the gale, as though nothing extraordinary were happening.

The Processionary: Meteorology

From the sum of my observations it appears
that the Pine Processionary is eminently sensitive to atmospheric vicissitudes, an excellent quality, having regard to his way of
life in the sharp winter nights. He foresees the storm which would imperil his
excursions.

His capacity for scenting bad weather very
soon won the confidence of the household.
When we had to go into Orange to renew our
provisions, it became the rule to consult him
the night before; and, according to his verdict, we went or stayed at home. His oracle
never deceived us. In the same way, simple
folk that we were, we used in the old days
to interrogate the Dor-beetle,[1] another
doughty nocturnal worker. But, a little de-
moralized by imprisonment in a cage and apparently devoid of any special sensitive apparatus, performing his evolutions, moreover,
in the mild autumn evenings, the celebrated
Dung-beetle could never rival the Pine Caterpillar, who is active during the roughest season of the year and endowed, as everything

[1] *Geotrupes stercorarius,* a large Dung-beetle. Cf. *The
Life and Love of the Insect,* by J. Henri Fabre, translated
by Alexander Teixeira de Mattos: chap. ix—*Translator's
Note.*

would seem to affirm, with organs quick to perceive the great atmospheric fluctuations.

Rural lore abounds in meteorological forecasts derived from animals. The Cat, sitting in front of the fire and washing behind her ears with a saliva-smeared paw, foretells another cold snap; the Cock, crowing at unusual hours, announces the return of fine weather; the Guinea-fowl, with her screeching, as of a scythe on the grindstone, points to rain; the Hen, standing on one leg, her plumage ruffled, her head sunk on her neck, feels a hard frost coming; the pretty green Tree-frog inflates his throat like a bladder at the approach of a storm and, according to the Provençal peasant, says:

"*Ploùra, ploùra;* it will rain, it will rain!"

This rustic meteorology, the heritage of the centuries, does not show up so badly beside our scientific meteorology.

Are not we ourselves living barometers? Every veteran complains of his glorious scars when the weather is about to break. One man, though unwounded, suffers from insomnia or from bad dreams; another, though a brain-worker, cannot drag an idea out of his impotent head. Each of us, in

The Processionary: Meteorology

his own way, is tried by the passage of those huge funnels which form in the atmosphere and hatch the storm.

Could the insect, with its exceptionally delicate organization, escape this kind of impression? It is unbelievable. The insect, more than any other ceature, should be an animated meteorological instrument, as truthful in its forecasts, if we knew how to read them, as the lifeless instruments of our observatories, with their mercury and their catgut. All, in different degrees, possess a general impressionability analogous to our own and exercised without the aid of specific organs. Some, better-gifted because of their mode of life, might well be furnished with special meteorological apparatus.

The Pine Processionary seems to belong to this number. In his second costume, when the segments bear on their dorsal faces an elegant red mosaic, he differs apparently from other caterpillars only by a more delicate general impressionability, unless this mosaic be endowed with aptitudes unknown elsewhere. If the nocturnal spinner is still none too generously equipped, it must be remembered that the season which he passes in this condition is nearly always clement. The really formidable nights hardly set in before January. But then, as a safeguard in his peregrinations, the Pine Processionary cleaves his back with a series of mouths which yawn open to sample the air from time to time and to give a warning of the sudden storm.

Until further evidence is forthcoming, therefore, the dorsal slits are, to my mind, meteorological instruments, barometers influenced by the main fluctuations of the atmosphere. To go beyond suspicions, though these are well based, is for me impossible. I lack the equipment necessary to delve more deeply into the subject. But I have given a hint. It is for those who are better favoured in the matter of resources to find the final solution of this interesting problem.

CHAPTER V

THE PINE PROCESSIONARY: THE MOTH

WHEN March comes, the caterpillars reared in domesticity never cease processioning. Many leave the greenhouse, which remains open; they go in search of a suitable spot for the approaching metamorphosis. This is the final exodus, the definite abandonment of the nest and the pine-tree. The pilgrims are much faded, whitish, with a few russet hairs on their backs.

On the 20th of March I spend a whole morning watching the evolutions of a file some three yards in length, containing about a hundred emigrants. The procession toils grimly along, undulating over the dusty ground, where it leaves a furrow. Then it breaks into a small number of groups, which crowd together and remain quiescent save for sudden oscillations of the hind-quarters. After a halt of varying duration, these groups resume their march, henceforward forming independent processions.

They take no settled direction. This one

goes forward, that one goes back; one turns
to the left and another to the right. There
is no rule about their marching, no positive
goal. One procession, after describing a loop,
retraces its steps. Yet there is a general tend-
ency towards that wall of the greenhouse
which faces the south and reflects the sun's
rays with added fervour. The sole guide, it
would seem, is the amount of sun which a
place obtains; the directions whence the greatest heat comes are preferred.

After a couple of hours of marching and
countermarching, the fragmentary processions, comprising each a score of caterpillars,
reach the foot of the wall. Here the soil
is powdery, very dry, easy to burrow in, although made somewhat firmer by tufts of
grass. The caterpillar at the head of the row
explores with his mandibles, digs a little, in-
vestigates the nature of the ground. The
others, trusting their leader, follow him with
docility, making no attempts of their own.
Whatever the foremost decides will be
adopted by all. Here, in the choice of a matter so important as the spot whereat the transformation shall take place, there is no individual initiative. There is only one will,

the leader's. There is only one head, so to
speak; the procession may be compared with
the chain of segments of an enormous worm.

Finally some spot is recognized as propitious. The leading caterpillar halts, pushes
with his head, digs with his mandibles. The
others, still in a continuous line, arrive one by
one and likewise come to a halt. Then the
file breaks up into a swarming heap, in which
each of the caterpillars resumes his liberty.
All their backs are joggling pell-mell; all their
heads are plunged into the dust; all their feet
are raking, all their mandibles excavating the
soil. The worm has chopped itself into a
gang of independent workers.

An excavation is formed in which, little by
little, the caterpillars bury themselves. For
some time to come, the undermined soil cracks
and rises and covers itself with little mole-
hills; then all is still. The caterpillars have
descended to a depth of three inches. This
is as far as the roughness of the soil permits
them to go. In looser soil, the excavation
would attain a much greater depth. The
greenhouse shelf, supplied with fine sand, has
provided me with cocoons placed at a depth
of from eight to twelve inches. I would not

assert that the interment might not be made still lower down. For the most part, the burial is effected in common, by more or less numerous clusters and at depths which vary greatly, according to the nature of the soil.

A fortnight later, let us dig at the point where the descent underground was made. Here we shall find the cocoons assembled in bunches, cocoons of sorry appearance, soiled as they are with earthy particles held by silken threads. When stripped of their rough exterior, they are not without a certain elegance. They are narrow ellipsoids, pointed at both ends, measuring twenty-five millimetres in length and nine millimetres[1] in thickness. The silk of which they are composed is very fine and of a dull white. The fragility of the walls is remarkable when we have seen the enormous quantity of silk expended on the construction of the nest.

A prodigious spinner where his winter habitation is concerned, the caterpillar finds his glands exhausted and is reduced to the strictly necessary amount when the time comes for making the cocoon. Too poor in silk, he strengthens his flimsy cell with a facing of

[1] .975 by .351 inch.—*Translator's Note.*

The Processionary: the Moth

earth. With him it is not the industry of the Bembex,[1] who inserts grains of sand in her silky web and makes a solid casket of the whole; it is a summary sort of art, devoid of delicacy, which just casually sticks together the surrounding earthy refuse.

Moreover, if circumstances demand it, the Pine Caterpillar can do without earth. In the very midst of the nest I have sometimes —very rarely, it is true—discovered cocoons which were perfectly clean. Not a scrap of alien matter defiled their fine white silk. I have obtained similar specimens by placing caterpillars under a bell-glass in a pan provided only with a few pine-twigs. Better still: an entire procession, a good-sized one too, gathered at the opportune moment and enclosed in a large box containing no sand nor any material whatever, spun its cocoons with no other support than the bare walls. These exceptions, provoked by circumstances in which the caterpillar is not free to act according to his wont, does not in any way invalidate the rule. To prepare for the transformation, the Processionary buries himself,

[1] Cf. *The Hunting Wasps:* chaps. xiv to xvii.-*Translator's Note.*

to the depth of nine inches and more, if the soil permit.

Here a curious problem forces itself upon the observer's mind. How does the Moth contrive to ascend from the catacombs into which the caterpillar has descended? Not in the finery of her perfect state—the big wings with their delicate scales, the sweeping antenna-plumes—dare she brave the asperities of the soil, or she would issue thence all tattered, rumpled and unrecognizable. And this is not the case: far from it. Moreover, what means can she employ, she so feeble, to break the crust of earth into which the original dust will have turned after the slightest of showers?

The Moth appears at the end of July or in August. The burial took place in March. Rain must have fallen during this lapse of time, rain which beats down the soil, cements it and leaves it to harden once evaporation has set in. Never could a Moth, unless attired and equipped with tools for the purpose, break her way through such an obstacle. She would perforce require a boring-tool and a costume of extreme simplicity. Guided by these considerations, I institute a few experiments which will give me the key to the riddle.

In April I make a copious collection of cocoons. Of these I place ten or twelve at the bottom of test-tubes of different diameters and, last of all, I fill the apparatus with sandy soil, sifted and very slightly moistened. The contents are pressed down, but in moderation, for fear of injuring the cocoons below. When the month of August comes, the column of earth, damp at the outset, has set so firmly, thanks to evaporation, that, when I reverse the test-tube, nothing trickles out. On the other hand, some cocoons have been kept naked under a metallic cover. These will teach me what the buried cocoons would not be able to show. They furnish me, in fact, with records of the greatest interest. On issuing from the cocoon, the Pine Bombyx has her finery bundled up and presents the appearance of a cylinder with rounded ends. The wings, the principal obstacle to underground labour, are pressed against the breast like narrow scarves; the antennæ, another serious embarrassment, have not yet unfolded their plumes and are turned back along the Moth's sides. The hair, which later forms a dense fleece, is laid flat, pointing backwards. The legs alone are free, fairly active and endowed with a certain vigour. Thanks to this arrangement, which does away with all awkward projections, the ascent through the soil is made possible.

True, every Moth, at the moment of quitting her shell, is this sort of swathed mummy; but the Pine Bombyx has in addition an exceptional aptitude rendered necessary by the fact that she hatches under the ground. While the others, once out of the cocoon, hasten to spread their wings and are powerless to defer their development, she, by virtue of an indispensable privilege, remains in her compact and wrapped-up condition as long as circumstances demand it. Under my bell-glasses I see some who, though born upon the surface, for twenty-four hours drag themselves over the sand or cling to the pine-branches, before untying their sashes and unfurling them as wings.

This delay is evidently essential. To ascend from beneath the earth and reach the open air, the Moth has to bore a long tunnel, which requires time. She will take good care not to spread her finery before emer-

ging, for it would hamper her and would itself be rumpled and badly creased. Therefore the cylindrical mummy persists until the
deliverance is effected; and, if liberty happen
to be acquired before the appointed moment,
the final evolution does not take place until
after a lapse of time in conformity with
usage.

We are acquainted with the equipment
for emergence, the tight-fitting jerkin indispensable in a narrow gallery. Now,
where is the boring-tool? The legs, though
free, would here be insufficient: they
would scrape the earth laterally, enlarging the diameter of the shaft, but could
not prolong the exit vertically, above the
insect's head. This tool must be in
front.

Pass the tip of your finger over the Moth's
head. You will feel a few very rough
wrinkles. The magnifying-glass shows us
more. We find, between the eyes and higher
up, four or five transversal scales, so set as
to overlap one another; they are hard and
black and are trimmed crescent-wise at the
ends. The longest and strongest is the upper-
most, which is in the middle of the forehead.

The Life of the Caterpillar

There you have the centre-bit of your boring-tool.

To make our tunnels in granitic rocks we tip our drills with diamond points. For a similar task the Bombyx, a living drill, wears implanted on her forehead a row of crescents, hard and durable as steel, a regular twist-bit. Without suspecting its use, Réaumur was perfectly aware of this marvellous implement, which he called scaly stairs:

"What does it profit this Moth," he asks, "that she should thus have the front of her head formed like scaly stairs? That is just what I do not know."

My test-tubes, learned master, will tell us. By good fortune, of the numerous Moths ascending from the bottom of my apparatus through a column of sand solidified by the evaporation of the original moisture, some are making their way upwards against the side of the tube, enabling me to follow their manœuvres. I see them raising their cylindrical bodies, butting with their heads, jerking now in one direction, now in another. The nature of their task is obvious. The centre-bits, with an alternating movement, are boring into the agglutinated sand. The powdery wreckage trickles down from overhead and is at once thrust backward by the legs. A little space forms at the top of the vault; and the Moth moves so much nearer to the surface. By the following day, the whole column, ten inches in height, will be perforated with a straight, perpendicular shaft.

Shall we now form an idea of the total work performed? Let us turn the test-tube upside down. The contents, as I have said, will not fall out, for they have set into a block; but from the tunnels bored by the Moth trickles all the sand crumbled by the crescents of the drill. The result is a cylindrical gallery, of the width of a lead-pencil, very cleanly cut and reaching to the bottom of the solid mass.

Are you satisfied, my master? Do you now perceive the great utility of the scaly stairs? Would you not say that we have here a magnificent example of an instrument superlatively fitted for a definite task? I share this opinion, for I think, with you, that a sovereign Reason has in all things coordinated the means and the end.

But let me tell you: we are called oldfashioned, you and I; with our conception of

The Life of the Caterpillar

a world ruled by an Intelligence, we are quite out of the swim. Order, balance, harmony: that is all silly nonsense. The universe is a fortuitous arrangement in the chaos of the possible. What is white might as easily be black, what is round might be angular, what is regular might be shapeless and harmony might just as well be discord. Chance has decided all things.

Yes, we are a pair of prejudiced old fogeys when we linger with a certain fondness over the marvels of perfection. Who troubles about these futilities nowadays? So-called serious science, the science which spells honour, profit and renown, consists in slicing your animal with very costly instruments into tiny circular sections. My housekeeper does as much with a bunch of carrots, with no higher pretention than to concoct a modest dish, which is not an invariable success. In the problem of life are we more successful when we have split a fibre into four and cut a cell into shavings? It hardly seems so. The riddle is as dark as ever. Ah, how much better is your method, my dear master; above all, how much loftier your philosophy, how much more wholesome and invigorating!

The Processionary: the Moth

Here at last is the Moth at the surface.
With the deliberate slowness demanded by so
delicate an operation, she spreads her bunched
wings, extends her antennæ and puffs out her
fleece. Her costume is a modest one: upper
wings grey, striped with a few crinkly brown
streaks; under-wings white; thorax covered
with thick grey fur; abdomen clad in bright-
russet velvet. The last segment has a pale-
gold sheen. At first sight it appears bare.
It is not, however; but, in place of hairs like
those of the other segments, it has, on its dorsal surface, scales so well assembled and so
close together that the whole seems to form a
continuous block, like a nugget.

Let us touch this trinket with the point of
a needle. However gently we rub, a multitude of scales come off and flutter at the least
breath, shining like mica spangles. Their
concave form, their shape, an elongated oval,
their colouring, white in the lower half but
reddish gold in the upper, give them, if we
allow for the difference in size, a certain resemblance to the scales surrounding the heads
of some of the centaury tribe. Such is the
golden fleece of which the mother will de-
spoil herself in order to cover the cylinder of

her eggs. The nugget of her hind-quarters, exfoliated spangle by spangle, will form a roof for the germs arranged like the grain in a corn-cob.

I was anxious to watch the actual placing of these pretty tiles, which are fixed at the pale end with a speck of cement, leaving the coloured end free. Circumstances did not favour me. Inactive all day, motionless on some needle of the lower branches, the Moth, whose life is very short, moves only in the darkness of the night. Both her mating and egg-laying are nocturnal. On the morrow, all is finished: the Bombyx has lived. Under these conditions, it was impossible, by the doubtful beams of a lantern, to follow satisfactorily the labour of the mother on the pine-trees in the garden.

I was no more fortunate with the captives in my bell-glasses. A few did lay their eggs, but always at a very advanced hour of the night, an hour which found my vigilance at fault. The light of a candle and eyes heavy with sleep were of little avail when it came to analysing the subtle operations of the mother as she puts her scales in place. We

The Processionary: the Moth

will say nothing of the little that was imperfectly seen.

Let us close with a few words of sylvicultural practice. The Pine Processionary is a voracious caterpillar who, while respecting the terminal bud, protected by its scales and its resinous varnish, completely denudes the bough and imperils the tree by leaving it bald. The green pine-needles, that mane in which the vegetable vigour of the tree resides, are shorn to the roots. How are we to remedy this?

When consulted on the subject, the forest-ranger of my parish told me that the custom is to go from tree to tree with pruning-shears fitted on a long pole and to cut down the nests, afterwards burning them. The method is a troublesome one, for the silken purses are often at considerable heights. Moreover, it is not without danger. Attacked by the hairy dust, the destroyers soon experience intolerable discomfort, a torture of irritation which makes them refuse to continue the work. To my thinking it would be better to operate before the appearance of the nests.

The Pine Bombyx is a very bad flyer. Incapable of soaring, almost like the Silk-moth, she flutters about and blunders to earth again; and her best efforts barely succeed in bringing her to the lower branches, which almost drag along the ground. Here are deposited the cylinders of eggs, at a height of six feet at most. It is the young caterpillars who, from one provisional encampment to another, gradually ascend, attaining, stage by stage, the summits upon which they weave their final dwellings. Once we grasp this peculiarity, the rest is plain sailing.

In August we inspect the lower foliage of the tree: an easy examination, for it is carried on no higher than our heads. Towards the far end of the twigs it is easy to espy the Bombyx' eggs, packed into cylinders that resemble scaly catkins. Their size and their whitish colour make them show up amid the sombre green. Gathered with the double pine-needle that bears them, these cylinders are crushed under foot, a summary fashion of stamping out an evil before it spreads.

This I have done in the case of the few pine-trees in my enclosure. And the same might be done in the wider forest expanses and more especially in parks and gardens, where symmetrical foliation is one of the

great beauties of the tree. I will add that
it is wise to prune every bough that droops
to earth and to keep the foot of the conifer
bare to a height of six feet or so. In the absence of these lower stairs, the only ones that
the Bombyx with her clumsy flight can reach,
she will not be able to populate the tree.

CHAPTER VI

THE Pine Processionary has three cos-
tumes: that of infancy, a scanty, ragged
fleece, a mixture of black and white; that of
middle age, the richest of the three, when the
segments deck themselves on their dorsal surface with golden tufts and a mosaic of bare
patches, scarlet in colour; and that of maturity, when the rings are cleft by slits which
one by one open and close their thick lips,
champing and grinding their bristling russet
beards and chewing them into little pellets,
which are thrown out on the creature's sides
when the bottom of the pocket swells up like
a tumour.

When wearing this last costume, the caterpillar is very disagreeable to handle, or even
to observe at close quarters. I happened,
quite ·unexpectedly, to learn this more thoroughly than I wished.

After unsuspectingly passing a whole morning with my insects, stooping over them, **magnifying-glass** in hand, to examine the working of their slits, I found my forehead and eyelids suffering with redness for twenty-four hours and afflicted with an itching even more painful and persistent than that produced by the sting of a nettle. On seeing me come down to dinner in this sad plight, with my eyes reddened and swollen and my face unrecognizable, the family anxiously enquired what had happened to me and were not reassured until I told them of my mishap.

I unhesitatingly attribute my painful experience to the red hairs ground to powder and collected into flakes. My breath sought them out in the open pockets and carried them to my face, which was very near. The unthinking intervention of my hands, which now and again sought to ease the discomfort, merely aggravated the ill by spreading the irritating dust.

No, the search for truth on the back of the Processionary is not all sunshine. It was only after a night's rest that I found myself pretty well recovered, the incident having no further ill effects. Let us continue, however.

The Life of the Caterpillar

It is well to substitute premeditated experiments for chance facts.

The little pockets of which the dorsal slits form the entrance are encumbered, as I have said, with hairy refuse, either scattered or gathered into flakes. With the point of a paint-brush I collect, when they gape open, a little of their contents and rub it on my wrist or on the inside of my fore-arm.

I have not long to wait for the result. Soon the skin turns red and is covered with pale lenticular swellings, similar to those produced by a nettle-sting. Without being very sharp, the pain was extremely unpleasant. By the following day, itching, redness and lenticular swellings had all disappeared. This is the usual sequence of events; but let me not omit to say that the experiment does not always succeed. The efficacy of the fluffy dust appears subject to great variations.

There have been occasions when I have rubbed myself with the whole caterpillar, or with his cast skin, or with the broken hairs gathered on a paint-brush, without producing any unpleasant results. The irritant dust seems to vary in quality according to certain circumstances which I have not been able to discover.

From my various tests it is evident that the discomfort is caused by the delicate hairs which the lips of the dorsal mouths, gaping and closing again, never cease grinding, to the detriment of their beards and moustaches. The edges of these slits, as their bristles rub off, furnish the stinging dust.

Having established this fact, let us proceed to more serious experiments. In the middle of March, when the Processionaries for the most part have migrated underground, I decide to open a few nests, as I wish to collect their last inhabitants for the purpose of my investigations. Without taking any precautions, my fingers tug at the silken dwelling, which is made of solid stuff; they tear it into shreds, search it through and through, turn it inside out and back again.

Once more and this time in a more serious fashion, I am the victim of my unthinking enthusiasm. Hardly is the operation completed, when the tips of my fingers begin to hurt in good earnest, especially in the more delicate part protected by the edge of the nail. The feeling is like the sharp pain of a sore that is beginning to fester. All the rest of the day and all through the night, the pain persists, troublesome enough to rob me of my sleep. It does not quiet down until the following day, after twenty-four hours of petty torment.

How did this new misadventure befall me? I had not handled the caterpillars: indeed, there were very few of them in the nest at the time. I had come upon no shed skins, for the moults do not take place inside the silken purse. When the moment has come to doff the second costume, that of the red mosaic, the caterpillars cluster outside, on the dome of their dwelling, and there leave in a single heap their old clothes entangled with bits of silk. What is left to explain the unpleasant consequences to which the handling of the nest exposes us?

The broken red bristles are left, the fallen hairs forming a dust that is invisible without a very careful examination. For a long time the Processionaries crawl and swarm about the nest; they pass to and fro, penetrating the thickness of the wall when they go to the pastures and when they return to their dormitory. Whether motionless or

The Stinging Power

on the move, they are constantly opening and closing their apparatus of information, the dorsal mouths. At the moment of closing, the lips of these slits, rolling on each other like the cylinders of a flattening-mill, catch hold of the fluff near them, tear it out and break it into fragments which the bottom of the pocket, presently reascending, shoots outside.

Thus myriads of irritant particles are disseminated and subtly introduced into every part of the nest. The shirt of Nessus burnt the veins of whoso wore it; the silk of the Processionary, another poisoned fabric, sets on fire the fingers that handle it.

The loathsome hairs long retain their virulence. I was once sorting out some handfuls of cocoons, many of which were diseased. As the hardness of the contents was usually an indication that something was wrong, I tore open the doubtful cocoons with my fingers, in order to save the non-contaminated chrysalids. My sorting was rewarded with the same kind of pain, especially under the edges of the nails, as I had already suffered when tearing the nests.

The cause of the irritation on this occasion was sometimes the dry skin discarded by the

The Life of the Caterpillar

Processionary on becoming a chrysalis and sometimes the shrivelled caterpillar turned into a sort of chalky cylinder through the invasion of the malignant fungus. Six months later, these wretched cocoons were still capable of producing redness and irritation.

Examined under the microscope, the russet hairs, the cause of the itching, are stiff rods, very sharp at either end and armed with barbs along the upper half. Their structure has absolutely nothing in common with nettle-hairs, those tapering phials whose hard point snaps off, pouring an irritant fluid into the tiny wound.

The plant from whose Latin name, *Urtica,* we derive the word urtication borrowed the design of its weapon from the fangs of the venomous serpents; it obtains its effect, not by the wound, but by the poison introduced into the wound. The Processionary employs a different method. The hairs, which have naught resembling the ampullary reservoir of the nettle-hairs, must be poisoned on the surface, like the assegais of the Kafirs and Zulus.

Do they really penetrate the epidermis? Are they like the savage's javelin, which cannot be extracted once it has gone in? With their barbs, do they enter all the more deeply because of the quivering of the outraged flesh? There is no ground for believing anything of the kind. In vain do I scrutinize the injured spot through the magnifying-glass; I can see no sign of the implanted dart. Neither could Réaumur, when an encounter with the Oak Processionary set him scratching himself. He had his suspicions, but could state nothing definitely.

No; despite their sharp points and their barbs, which make them, under the microscope, such formidable spears, the Processionary's russet hairs are not darts designed to imbed themselves in the skin and to provoke irritation by pricking.

Many caterpillars, all most inoffensive, have a coat of bristles which, under the microscope, resolve themselves into barbed javelins, quite harmless in spite of their threatening aspect. Let me mention a couple of these peaceable halberdiers.

Early in spring, we see, crossing the paths, a briskly-moving caterpillar who inspires repunance by his ferocious hairiness, which ripples like ripe corn. The ancient naturalists, with

The Life of the Caterpillar

their artless and picturesque nomenclature, called him the Hedgehog. The term is worthy of the creature, which, in the moment of danger, rolls itself up like a Hedgehog, presenting its spiny armour on all sides to the enemy. On its back is a dense mixture of black hairs and hairs of ashen-gray; while on the sides and fore-part of the body is a stiff mane of bright russet. Black, grey or russet, all this fierce-looking coat is heavily barbed.

One hesitates to touch this horror with the finger-tips. Still, encouraged by my example, seven-year-old Paul, with his tender child's skin, gathers handfuls of the repulsive insect with no more apprehension than if he were picking a bunch of violets. He fills his boxes with it; he rears it on elm-leaves and handles it daily, for he knows that from this frightful creature he will one day obtain a superb Moth (*Chelonia caja,* LINN.), clad in scarlet velvet, with the lower wings red and the upper white, sprinkled with brown spots.

What resulted from the child's familiarity with the shaggy creature? Not even a trace of itching on his delicate skin. I do not speak of mine, which is tanned by the years.

In the osier-beds of our local stream, the

The Stinging Power

rushing Aygues, a thorny shrub abounds which, at the advent of autumn, is covered with an infinity of very sour red berries. Its crabbed boughs, which bear but little verdure, are hidden under their clusters of vermilion balls. It is the sallow thorn or sea buckthorn *(Hippophaë rhamnoides)*.

In April, a very hairy but rather pretty caterpillar lives at the expense of this shrub's budding leaves. He has on his back five dense tufts of hair, set side by side and arranged like the bristles of a brush, tufts deep-black in the centre and white at the edges. He waves two divergent plumes in front of him and sports a third on his crupper, like a feathery tail. These three are black hair-pencils of extreme delicacy.

His greyish Moth, flattened motionless on the bark, stretches his long fore-legs, one against the other, in front of him. You would take them, at a first glance, for antennae of exaggerated proportions. This pose of the extended limbs has won the insect the scientific label of Orgyia, arm's length; and also the vulgar and more expressive denomination of *Patte étendue,* or outstretched paw.

Little Paul has not failed, with my aid, to

rear the pretty bearer of the tufts and brushes. How many times, with his sensitive finger, has he not stroked the creature's furry costume? He found it softer than velvet. And yet, enlarged under the microscope, the caterpillar's hairs are horrible barbed spears, no less menacing than those of the Processionary. The resemblance goes no farther: handled without precautions, the tufted caterpillar does not provoke even a simple rash. Nothing could be more harmless than his coat.

It is evident, then, that the cause of the irritation lies elsewhere than in the barbs. If the barbed bristles were enough to poison the fingers, most hairy caterpillars would be dangerous, for nearly all have spiny bristles. We find, on the contrary, that virulence is bestowed upon a very small number, which are not distinguished from the rest by any special structure of the hair.

That the barbs have a part to play, that of fixing the irritant atom upon the epidermis, of keeping it anchored in its place, is, after all, possible; but the shooting pains cannot by any means be caused by the mere prick of so delicate a harpoon.

Much less slender, the hairs clustered

138

into pads on the prickly pears are fero-
ciously barbed. Woe to the fingers that
handle this kind of velvet too confidently!
At the least touch they are pierced with har-
poons whose extraction involves a severe tax
upon our patience. Other inconvenience there
is little or none, for the action of the barb is
in this case purely mechanical. Supposing—a
very doubtful thing—that the Processionary's
hairs could penetrate our skin, they would act
likewise, only with less effect, if they had
merely their sharp points and their barbs.
What then do they possess in addition?

They must have, not inside them, like the
hairs of the nettle, but outside, on the surface,
an irritant agent; they must be coated with a
poisonous mixture, which makes them act by
simple contact.

Let us remove this virus, by means of a
solvent; and the Processionary's darts, reduced to their insignificant mechanical action,
will be harmless. The solvent, on the other
hand, rid of all hairs by filtration, will be
charged with the irritant element, which we
shall be able to test without the agency of the
hairs. Isolated and concentrated, the stinging element, far from losing by this treat-

ment, ought to gain in virulence. So reflection tells us.

The solvents tried are confined to three: water, spirits of wine and sulphuric ether. I employ the latter by preference, although the other two, spirits of wine especially, have yielded satisfactory results. To simplify the experiment, instead of submitting to the action of the solvent the entire caterpillar, who would complicate the extract with his fats and his nutritive juices, I prefer to employ the cast skin alone.

I therefore collect, on the one hand, the heap of dry skins which the moult of the second phase has left on the dome of the silken dwelling and, on the other hand, the skins which the caterpillars have rejected in their cocoons before becoming chrysalids; and I leave the two lots to infuse, separately, in sulphuric ether for twenty-four hours. The infusion is colourless. The liquid, carefully filtered, is exposed to spontaneous evaporation; and the skins are rinsed with ether in the filter, several times over.

There are now two tests to be made: one with the skins and one with the product of maceration. The first is as conclusive as can be. Hairy as in the normal state and perfectly dried, the skins of both lots, drained by the ether, produce not the slightest effect, although I rub myself with them, without the least caution, at the juncture of the fingers, a spot very sensitive to stinging.

The hairs are the same as before the action of the solvent: they have lost none of their barbs, of their javelin-points; and yet they are ineffectual. They produce no pain or inconvenience whatever. Deprived of their toxic smearing, these thousands of darts become so much harmless velvet. The Hedgehog Caterpillar and the Brush Caterpillar are not more inoffensive.

The second test is more positive and so conclusive in its painful effects that one hardly likes to try it a second time. When the ethereal infusion is reduced by spontaneous evaporation to a few drops, I soak in it a slip of blotting-paper folded in four, so as to form a square measuring something over an inch. Too unsuspecting of my product, I do things on a lavish scale, both as regards the superficial area of my poor epidermis and the quantity of the virus. To any one who might wish to renew the investigation I should recommend a less generous dose. Lastly, the square of paper, that novel sort of mustard-plaster, is applied to the under surface of the fore-arm. A thin waterproof sheeting covers it, to prevent it from drying too rapidly; and a bandage holds it in place.

For the space of ten hours, I feel nothing; then I experience an increasing itch and a burning sensation acute enough to keep me awake for the greater part of the night. Next day, after twenty-four hours of contact, the poultice is removed. A red mark, slightly swollen and very clearly outlined, occupies the square which the poisoned paper covered.

The skin feels sore, as though it had been cauterized, and looks as rough as shagreen. From each of its tiny pustules trickles a drop of serous fluid, which hardens into a substance similar in colour to gum-arabic. This oozing continues for a couple of days and more. Then the inflamation abates; the pain, hitherto very trying, quiets down; the skin dries and comes off in little flakes. All is over, except the red mark, which remains for a long time, so tenacious in its effects is this extract of Processionary. Three weeks after the experiment, the little square on the fore-arm subjected to the poison is still discoloured.

For thus branding one's self, does one at least obtain some small reward? Yes. A little truth is the balm spread upon the wound; and indeed truth is a sovran balm. It will come presently to solace us for much greater sufferings.

For the moment, this painful experiment shows us that the irritation has not as its primary cause the hairiness of the Processionary. Here is no hair, no barb, no dart. All of that has been retained by the filter. We have nothing now but a poisonous agent extracted by the solvent, the ether. This irritant element recalls, to a certain extent, that of cantharides, which acts by simple contact. My square of poisoned blotting-paper was a sort of plaster, which, instead of raising the epidermis in great blisters, makes it bristle with tiny pustules.

The part played by the barbed hairs, those atoms which the least movement of the air disseminates in all directions, is confined to conveying to our face and hands the irritant substance in which they are impregnated. Their barbs hold them in place and thus permit the virus to act. It is even probable that, by means of slight scratches which would otherwise pass unnoticed, they assist the action of the stinging fluid.

Shortly after handling the Processionaries, a delicate epidermis becomes tumefied, red and painful. Without being immediate, the action of the caterpillar is prompt. The extract made with ether, on the other hand, causes pain and rubefaction only after a longish interval. What does it need to produce more rapid ulceration? To all appearances, the action of the hairs.

The direct stinging caused by the caterpillar is nothing like so serious as that produced by the ethereal extract concentrated in a few drops. Never before, in my most painful misadventures, whether with the silken purses or their inhabitants, have I seen my skin covered with serous pustules and peeling off in flakes. This time it is a veritable sore, anything but pleasing to the eye.

The aggravation is easily explained. I soaked in the ether some fifty discarded skins. The few drops which remained after the evaporation and which were absorbed by the square of blotting-paper represented, there-

fore, the virulence of a single insect fifty
times increased. My little blistering-plaster
was equivalent to the contact of fifty caterpillars at the same spot. There is no doubt
that, if we left them to steep in considerable
numbers, we should obtain extracts of really
formidable strength. It is quite possible that
medical science will one day make good use
of this powerful counter-irritant, which is utterly different from cantharides.

Whether voluntary victims of our curiosity,
which, while affording no other satisfaction
than that of knowledge, exposes us to an intolerable itch, or sufferers through an accident,
what can we do to give a little relief to the
irritation caused by the Processionary? It is
good to know the origin of the evil, but it
would be better to apply a remedy.

One day, with both hands sore from the
prolonged examination of a nest, I try without
success lotions of alcohol, glycerine, oil and
soapsuds. Nothing does any good. I then
remember a palliative employed by Réaumur
against the sting of the Oak Processionary.
Without telling us how he came to know of
the strange specific, the master rubbed himself
with parsley and felt a good deal the better

for it. He adds that any other leaf would probably assuage the irritation in the same way.

This is a fitting occasion for reopening the subject. Here, in a corner of the garden, is parsley, green and abundant as one could wish. What other plant can we compare with it? I choose the purslain, the spontaneous guest of my vegetable-beds. Mucilaginous and fleshy as it is, it readily crushes, yielding an emollient liniment. I rub one hand with parsley and the other with purslain, pressing hard enough to reduce the leaves to a paste. The result deserves attention.

With the parsley, the burning is a little less acute, it is true, but, though relieved, it persists for a long time yet and continues troublesome. With the purslain, the petty torture ceases almost at once and so completely that I no longer notice it. My nostrum possesses incontestable virtues. I recommend it quietly, without blatant advertisement, to any one who may be persecuted by the Processionary. Foresters, in their war upon caterpillars' nests, should find great relief from it.

I have also obtained good results with the leaves of the tomato and the lettuce; and, without pursuing this botanical survey further, I remain convinced, with Réaumur, that any tender juicy foliage would possess a certain efficacy.

As for the mode of action of this specific, I admit that I do not understand it, any more than I can perceive the mode of action of the caterpillar's virus. Molière's medical student explained the soporific properties of opium by saying:

"Quia est in eo virtus dormitava cujus est proprietas sensus assoupire."

Let us say likewise: the crushed herb calms the burning itch because it possesses a calming virtue whose property is to assuage itching.

The quip is a good deal more philosophical than it looks. What do we know of our remedies or of anything? We perceive effects, but we cannot get back to their causes.

In my village and for some distance around it, there is a popular belief that to relieve the pain of a Wasp's or Bee's sting all that we need do is to rub the part stung with three sorts of herbs. Take, they say, three kinds of herbs, the first that come to hand, make them into a bunch and rub hard. The prescription, by all accounts, is infallible.

I thought at first that this was one of those therapeutic absurdities which have their birth in rustic imaginations. After making a trial, I admit that what sounds like a nonsensical remedy sometimes has something genuine about it. Friction with three kinds of herbs does actually deaden the sting of the Wasp or Bee.

I hasten to add that the same success is achieved with a single herb; and so the result agrees with what the parsley and purslain have taught us in respect of the irritation caused by the Processionary.

Why three herbs when one is enough? Three is the preeminently lucky number; it smacks of witchcraft, which is far from detracting from the virtues of the unguent. All rustic medicine has a touch of magic about it; and there is merit in doing things by threes.

Perhaps the specific of the three herbs may even date back to the *materia medica* of antiquity. Dioscorides recommends τρίφυλλον: it is, he states, good for the bite of venomous serpents. To determine this celebrated three-leaved plant exactly would not be easy. Is it a common clover? The psoralea, with its pitchy odour? The menyanthes, or uck-bean, that inmate of the chilly peat-bogs? The oxalis, the wood-sorrel of the country-side? We cannot tell for certain. The botany of those days was innocent of the descriptive conscientiousness of ours. The plant which acted as a poison-antidote grouped its leaves by threes. That is its essential characteristic.

Again the cabalistic number, essential to medical virtues as conceived by the first healers. The peasant, a tenacious conservative, has preserved the ancient remedy, but, by a happy inspiration, has changed the three original leaves into three different herbs; he has elaborated the $\tau\rho\iota\varphi\upsilon\lambda\lambda\upsilon$ into the threefold foliage which he crushes on the Bee's sting. I seem to perceive a certain relation between these artless ways and the crushing of parsley as described by Réaumur.

CHAPTER VII

THE ARBUTUS CATERPILLAR

I HAVE not found many species of urticating caterpillars in the small corner of my
investigations. I know of two only: the Pine
Caterpillar and the Arbutus Caterpillar. The
latter belongs to the genus Liparis. His
Moth, who is a glorious snowy white, with
the last rings of the abdomen bright russet,
is very like *Liparis auriflua,* FAB., from whom
she differs not only in size—she is smaller—
but, above all, in the field of operations selected by her caterpillar. Is the species class-
ified in our lists? I do not know; and really
it is hardly worth while to enquire. What
does a Latin name matter, when one cannot
mistake the insect? I shall be sparing of detail concerning the Arbutus Caterpillar, for
he is far less interesting in his habits than the
Pine Processionary. Only his ravages and his
poison deserve serious attention.

On the Sérignan hills, sunny heights upon
which the Mediterranean vegetation comes
to an end, the arbutus, or strawberry-tree,

The Arbutus Caterpillar

abounds: a magnificent shrub, with lustrous evergreen foliage, vermilion fruit, round and fleshy as strawberries, and hanging clusters of little white bells resembling those of the lily of the valley. When the frosts come at the approach of December, nothing could be more charming than the arbutus, decking its gay verdure with both fruits and flowers, with coral balls and plump little bells. Alone of our flora, it combines the flowering of to-day with the ripening of yesterday.

Then the bright-red raspberries—the *darbouses,* as we call them here—beloved by the Blackbird, grow soft and sweet to the palate. The housewives pluck them and make them into preserves that are not without merit. As for the shrub itself, when the season for cutting has come, it is not, despite its beauty, respected by the woodman. It serves, like any trivial brushwood, in the making of faggots for heating ovens. Frequently, too, the showy arbutus is ravaged by a caterpillar yet more to be dreaded than the woodcutter. After this glutton has been at it, it could not look more desolate had it been scorched and blackened by fire.

The Moth, a pretty little, snow-white Bom-

byx, with superb antennary plumes and a cotton-wool tippet on her thorax, lays her eggs
on a leaf of the arbutus and, in so doing,
starts the evil.

You see a little cushion with pointed ends,
rather less than an inch in length; a white
eiderdown, tinged with russet, thick, very soft
and formed of hairs fixed with a little gum by
the end that points towards the upper extremity of the leaf. The eggs are sunk in
the thickness of this soft shelter. They possess a metallic sheen and look like so many
nickel granules.

Hatching takes place in September. The
first meals are made at the expense of the
native leaf; the later ones at the expense of
the leaves all around. One surface only is
nibbled, usually the upper; the other remains
intact, trellised by the network of veins,
which are too horny for the new-born grubs.

The consumption of leaves is effected with
scrupulous economy. Instead of grazing at
hazard and using up the pasturage at the dic-
tates of individual caprice, the flock progresses
gradually from the base to the tip of the leaf,
with all heads ranged in a frontal attack,
almost in a straight line. Not a bite is taken

beyond this line, until all that lies on this side of it is eaten up.

As it advances, the flock throws a few threads across the denuded portion, where nothing remains but the veins and the epidermis of the opposite surface. Thus is woven a gossamer veil serving as a shelter from the fierce rays of the sun and as the parachute which is essential to these weaklings, whom a puff of wind would carry away.

As the result of a more rapid desiccation on the ravaged surface, the leaf soon begins to curl of its own accord, curving into a gondola which is covered by a continuous awning stretched from end to end. The herbage is then exhausted. The flock abandons it and begins again elsewhere in the near neighbourhood.

After various temporary pastures of this kind, in November, when the cold weather is at hand, the caterpillars settle permanently at the end of a bough. Nibbled one by one on their upper surfaces, the leaves of the terminal bunch draw close to their neighbours, which, excoriated in their turn, do the same, until the whole forms a bundle, which looks as if it had been scorched, lashed together with mag-

The Life of the Caterpillar

nificent white silk. This is the winter habitation, whence the family, still very feeble, will not issue until the fine weather returns.

The assembling of this leafy framework is not due to any special industry on the caterpillars' part; they do not stretch their threads from leaf to leaf and then, by pulling at these ropes, bring the various pieces of the structure into contact. It is merely the result of desiccation on the nibbled surfaces. Fixed cables, it is true, solidly bind together the leaves brought close to one another by the contraction due to their aridity; but they do not in any way play the part of a motive mechanism in the work of the assemblage.

No hauling-ropes are here, no capstans to move the timbers. The feeble creatures would be incapable of such effort. The thing happens of itself. Sometimes a floating thread, the plaything of the air, enlaces some adjacent leaf. This chance footbridge tempts the explorers, who hasten to strip the accidental prize; and, without other labour, yet one more leaf bends of its own accord and is added to the enclosure. For the most part, the house is built by eating; a lodging is procured by dint of banqueting.

154

The Arbutus Caterpillar

A comfortable house, tightly closed and well-caulked, proof against rain and snow. We, to guard ourselves against draughts, put sand-bags against the cracks of our doors and windows; the extravagant little Arbutus Caterpillar applies pipings of silk-velvet to his shutters. Things should be cosy inside, however damp the fog. In bad weather, the rain drips into my house. (The leaf-dwelling knows nothing of such troubles, so true is it that animals often enjoy advantages which relegate human industry to the second rank.)

In this shelter of silk and foliage, the worst three or four months of the year are passed in a state of complete abstinence. No outings; not a bite of food. In March, this torpor ceases; and the recluses, those starving bellies, shift their quarters.

The community now splits up into squads, which spread themselves anyhow over the adjacent verdure. This is the period of serious devastation. The caterpillars no longer confine themselves to nibbling one surface of the leaf; their keen appetites demand the whole of it, down to the stalk. And now, stage by stage, halt by halt, the arbutus is shorn bare.

The vagabonds do not return to their win-

The Life of the Caterpillar

ter dwelling, which has become too closely cramped. They reassemble in groups and weave, here, there and everywhere, shapeless tents, temporary huts, abandoned for others as the pasturage round about becomes exhausted. The denuded boughs, to all seeming ravaged by fire, take on the look of squalid drying-grounds hung with rags.

In June, having acquired their full growth, the caterpillars leave the arbutus-tree, descend to earth and spin themselves, amid the dead leaves, a niggardly cocoon, in which the insect's hairs to some extent supplement its silk. A month later, the Bombyx appears.

In his final dimensions, the caterpillar measures nearly an inch and a quarter in length. His costume does not lack richness or originality: a black skin with a double row of orange specks on the back; long grey hairs arranged in bunches; short, snow-white tufts on the sides; and a couple of brown-velvet protuberances on the first two rings of the abdomen and also on the last ring but one.

The most remarkable feature, however, consists of two tiny craters, always open wide; two cunningly fashioned goblets which might have been wrought from a drop of red seal-

The Arbutus Caterpillar

ing-wax. The sixth and seventh segments of
the abdomen are the only ones that bear these
vermilion goblets, placed in the middle of the
back. I do not know the function of these
little cups. Perhaps they should be regarded
as organs of information, similar to the Pine
Processionary's dorsal mouths.

The Arbutus Caterpillar is much dreaded
in the village. Woodcutters, faggot-binders,
brushwood-gatherers, all are unanimous in re-
viling him. They have such a painfully vivid
memory of the irritation that, when I listen
to them, I can hardly repress a movement of
the shoulders to relieve the imaginary itching
in the middle of my back. I seem to feel the
arbutus-faggot, laden with its glowing rags,
rubbing my bare skin.

It is, it appears, a disagreeable job to cut
down the shrub alive with caterpillars during
the hottest part of the day and to shake, under
the blows of the axe, that sort of upas-tree,
shedding poison in its shade. As for me, I
have no complaint to make of my relations
with the ravager of the arbutus. I have very
often handled him; I have applied his fur to
the tips of my fingers, my neck and even my
face, for hours at a time; I have ripped up

157

The Life of the Caterpillar

the nests to extract their populations for the purpose of my researches; but I have never been inconvenienced. Save in exceptional circumstances, the approach of the moult perhaps, this would need a skin less tough than mine.

The thin skin of a child does not enjoy the same immunity, as witness little Paul, who, having helped me to empty some nests and to collect the inhabitants with my forceps, was for hours scratching his neck, which was dotted with red wheals. My ingenuous assistant was proud of his sufferings in the cause of science, which resulted from heedlessness and also perhaps from bravado. In twenty-four hours, the trouble disappeared, without leaving any serious consequences.

All this hardly tallies with the painful experiences of which the woodcutters talk. Do they exaggerate? That is hardly credible; they are so unanimous. Then something must have been lacking in my experiments: the propitious moment apparently, the proper degree of maturity in the caterpillar, the high temperature which aggravates the poison.

To show itself in its full severity, the urtication demands the cooperation of certain undefined circumstances; and this cooperation was wanting. Chance perhaps will one day teach me more than I want to know; I shall be attacked in the manner familiar to the woodcutters and shall pass a night in torment, tossing and turning as though on a bed of live coals.

What the direct contact of the caterpillar did not teach me the artifices of chemistry will demonstrate with a violence which I was far from expecting. I treat the caterpillar with ether, just as I treated the slough of the Pine Processionary. The number of the creatures taken for the infusion—they are pretty small as yet, are scarcely half the size which they will attain when mature—is about a hundred. After a couple of days' maceration, I filter the liquid and leave it to evaporate freely. With the few drops that remain I soak a square of blotting-paper folded in four and apply it to the inner surface of my forearm, with a thin rubber sheet and a bandage. It is an exact repetition of what I did with the Pine Processionary.

Applied in the morning, the blister hardly takes effect until the following night. Then by degrees the irritation becomes unendurable;

The Life of the Caterpillar

and the burning sensation is so acute that I am tormented every moment with the desire to tear off the bandage. However, I hold out, but at the cost of a sleepless, feverish night.

How well I now understand what the woodcutters tell me! I had less than a square inch of skin subjected to the torture. What would it be if I had my back, shoulders, neck, face and arms tormented in this fashion? I pity you with all my heart, you labourers who are troubled by the hateful creature.

On the morrow, the infernal paper is removed. The skin is red and swollen, covered with tiny pimples whence ooze drops of serous fluid. For five days the itching persists, with a sharp, burning pain, and the running from the pimples continues. Then the dead skin dries and comes off in scabs. All is over, save the redness, which is still perceptible a month later.

The demonstration is accomplished; the Arbutus Caterpillar, capable as he is of producing, under certain conditions, the same effects which I obtain by artificial means, fully deserves his odious reputation.

CHAPTER VIII

AN INSECT VIRUS

ONE step forward has been taken, but only a very little one as yet, in the problem of the stinging caterpillars. The drenching with ether teaches us that hairiness plays a very secondary part in the matter. With its dust of broken bristles, which the least breath wafts in all directions, it bothers us by depositing and fixing its irritant coating upon us; but this virus does not originate in the creature's fleece; it comes from elsewhere. What is the source of it?

I will enter into a few details. Perhaps, in so doing, I shall be of service to the novice. The subject, which is very simple and sharply defined, will show us how one question gives rise to another; how experimental tests confirm or upset hypotheses, which are, as it were, a temporary scaffolding; and, lastly, how logic, that severe examiner, leads us by degrees to generalities which are far more important than anything that we were led to anticipate at the outset.

The Life of the Caterpillar

And, first of all, does the Pine Processionary possess a special glandular structure
which elaborates the virus, as do, for instance, the poison-glands of the Wasps and
Bees? By no means. Anatomy shows that
the internal structure of the stinging caterpillar is similar to that of the harmless one.
There is nothing more and nothing less.

The poisonous product, of unlocalized origin, results, therefore, from a general process
in which the entire organism is brought into
play. It should, in consequence, be found in
the blood, after the manner of urea in higher
animals. This is a suggestion of grave im-
port, but after all quite valueless without the
conclusive verdict of actual experiment.

Five or six Processionaries, pricked with
the point of a needle, furnish me with a few
drops of blood. I allow these to soak into a
small square of blotting-paper, which I then
apply to my fore-arm with a waterproof
bandage. It is not without a certain anxiety
that I await the outcome of the experiment.
The result will show whether the conclusions
already forming in my mind will receive a
solid basis or vanish into thin air.

At a late hour of the night, the pain wakes

An Insect Virus

me, a pain which this time is an intellectual joy. My anticipations were correct. The blood does indeed contain the venomous substance. It causes itching, swelling, a burning sensation, an exudation of serum and, lastly, a shedding of the skin. I learn more than I had hoped to learn. The test is more valuable than that of mere contact with the caterpillar could have been. Instead of treating myself with the small quantity of poison with which the hairs are smeared, I have gone to the source of the irritant substance and I thereby gain an increase of discomfort.

Very happy in my suffering, which sets me on a safe path, I continue my enquiry by arguing thus: the virus in the blood cannot be a living substance, one that takes part in the working of the organism; it is rather, like urea, a form of decay, an offthrow of the vital process, a waste product which is expelled as and when it forms. If this be the case, I ought to find it in the caterpillar's droppings, which are made up of both the digestive and the urinary residues.

Let us describe the new experiment, which is no less positive than the last. I leave a few pinches of very dry droppings, such as are found in abundance in the old nests, to soak for two days in sulphuric ether. The liquid, coloured as it is with the chlorophyll of the caterpillar's food, turns a dirty green. Then I repeat precisely the process which I mentioned when I wanted to prove the innocuousness of the hairs deprived of their poisonous varnish. I refer to it a second time in order thoroughly to explain the method pursued and to save repetition in the various experiments undertaken.

The infusion is filtered, spontaneously evaporated and reduced to a few drops, with which I soak my stinger. This consists of a small piece of blotting-paper, folded in four to increase the thickness of the pad and to give it a greater power of absorption. An area of a square inch or less suffices; in some cases it is even too much. A novice in this kind of research-work, I was too lavish with the liniment; and in return for my generosity I had such a bad time that I make a point of warning any reader desirous of repeating the experiment upon his own person.

Fully soaked, the square of paper is applied to the fore-arm, on the inner surface, where the skin is more tender. A sheet of rubber covers it and, being waterproof, guards against the loss of the poison. Finally, a linen bandage keeps the whole in place.

On the afternoon of the 4th of June 1897, a memorable date for me, I test, as I have just said, the etheric extract of the Processionary's droppings. All night long, I feel a violent itching, a burning sensation and shooting pains. On the following day, after twenty hours of contact, I remove the dressing.

The venomous liquid, too lavishly employed in my fear of failure, has considerably overflowed the limits of the square of paper. The parts which it has touched and still more the portion covered by the pad are swollen and very red; moreover, in the latter case, the skin is ridged, wrinkled and mortified. It smarts a little and itches; and that is all.

On the following day, the swelling becomes more pronounced and goes deep into the muscles, which, when touched with the finger, throb like an inflamed cheek. The colour is a bright carmine and extends all round the spot which the paper covered. This is due to the escape of some of the liquid. There is a plentiful discharge of serum, oozing from the sore in tiny drops. The smarting and itching increase and become so intense, especially during the night, that, to get a little sleep, I am driven to employ a palliative, vaseline with borax and a lint dressing.

In five days' time, it has developed into a hideous ulcer, which looks more painful than it really is. The red, swollen flesh, quivering and denuded of its epidermis, provokes commiseration. The person who night and morning renews my dressing of lint and vaseline is almost sick at the sight.

"One would think," she says, "that the dogs had been gnawing your arm. I do hope you won't try any more of those horrible decoctions."

I allow my sympathetic nurse to talk away and am already meditating further experiments, some of which will be equally painful. O sacred truth, what can rival thy power over us mortals! Thou turnest my petty torment into contentment; thou makest me rejoice in my flayed arm! What shall I gain by it all? I shall know why a wretched caterpillar sets us scratching ourselves. Nothing more; and that is enough for me.

Three weeks later, new skin is forming, but is covered all over with painful little pimples.

An Insect Virus

The swelling diminishes; the redness persists and is still very marked. The effect of the infernal paper lasts a long time. At the end of a month, I still feel an itching, a burning irritation, which is intensified by the warmth of the bed-clothes. At last, a fortnight later, all has disappeared but the redness, of which I shall retain the marks for a long time yet, though it grows gradually fainter and fainter. It will take three months or more to vanish altogether.

We now have some light on the problem: the Processionary's virus is certainly an off-throw of the organic factory, a waste product of the living edifice. The caterpillar discards it with his excrement. But the material of the droppings has a twofold origin: the greater part represents the digestive residuum; the rest, in a much smaller proportion, is composed of the urinary products. To which of the two does the virus belong? Before going farther, let us permit ourselves a digression which will assist us in our subsequent enquiries. Let us ask what advantages the Processionary derives from his urticating product.

I already hear the answer:

"It is a means of protection, of defence.

The Life of the Caterpillar

With his poisoned mane, he repels the
enemy."

I do not clearly perceive the bearing of this
explanation. I think of the creature's recognized enemies: of the larva of *Calosoma
sycophanta,* which lives in the nests of the
Processionary of the Oak and gobbles up the
inhabitants with never a thought of their burning fleece; of the Cuckoo, another mighty consumer, so we are told, of the same caterpillars,
who gorges on them to the point of implant-
ing in his gizzard a bristling coat of their
hairs.

I am not aware if the Processionary of
the Pine pays a like tribute. I do know of
at least one of his exploiters. This is a
Dermestes,[1] who establishes himself in the
silken city and feeds upon the remains of the
defunct caterpillars. This ghoul assures us
of the existence of other consumers, all furnished with stomachs expressly fashioned for
such highly-seasoned fare. For every harvest of living creatures there is always a har-
vester.

No, the theory of a special virus, expressly
prepared to defend the Processionary and his

[1] A Bacon-beetle.—*Translator's Note.*

emulators in urtication, is not the last word on the subject. I should find it difficult to believe in such a prerogative. Why have these caterpillars, more than others, need of protection? What reasons would make of them a caste apart, endowed with an exceptional defensive venom? The part which they play in the entomological world does not differ from that of other caterpillars, hairy or smooth. It is the naked caterpillars who, in default of a mane capable of striking awe into the assailant, ought, one would think, to arm themselves against danger and impregnate themselves with corrosives, instead of remaining a meek and easy prey. Is it likely that the shaggy, bristling caterpillar should anoint his fleece with a formidable cosmetic and his smooth-coated kinsman be unfamiliar with the chemical properties of the poison beneath his satin skin! These contradictions do not inspire confidence.

Have we not here, rather, a property common to all caterpillars, smooth-skinned or hairy? Among the latter, there might be some, just a few, who, under certain special conditions which will need to be defined, would be quick to reveal by urtication the

The Life of the Caterpillar

venomous nature of their organic refuse; the others, the vast majority, living outside these conditions, even though endowed with the necessary product, would be inexpert at the stinging business and would not produce irritation by contact. In all, the same virus is to be found, resulting from an identical vital process. Sometimes it is brought into prominence by the itching which it produces; sometimes, indeed most often, it remains latent, unrecognized, if our artifices do not intervene.

What shall these artifices be? Something very simple. I address myself to the Silkworm. If there be an inoffensive caterpillar in the world, it is certainly he. Women and children take him up by the handful in our Silkworm-nurseries; and their delicate fingers are none the worse for it. The satin-skinned caterpillar is perfectly innocuous to a skin almost as tender as his own.

But this lack of caustic venom is only apparent. I treat with ether the excretions of the Silkworm; and the infusion, concentrated into a few drops, is tested according to the usual method. The result is wonderfully definite. A smarting sore on the arm, similar in its mode of appearance and in its effects to

An Insect Virus

that produced by the droppings of the Processionary, assures me that logic was right.

Yes, the virus which makes one scratch so much, which blisters and eats away the skin, is not a defensive product vested in only a few caterpillars. I recognize it, with its invariable properties, even in a caterpillar which at first sight appears as though it could not possess anything of the kind.

The Silkworm's virus, besides, is not unknown in my village. The casual observation of the peasant-woman has outstripped the precise observation of the man of science. The women and girls entrusted with the rearing of the Silkworm—the *magnanarelles* as they are called—complain of certain tribulations caused, they say, by *lou verin di magnan,* the Silkworms' poison. This trouble consists of a violent itching of the eyelids, which become red and swollen. In the case of the more susceptible, there is a rash and the skin peels off the fore-arm, which the turned-up sleeves fail to protect during work.

I now know the cause of this little trouble, my plucky *magnanarelles.* It is not contact with the worm that afflicts you; you need have no fear of handling him. It is only the litter that you need distrust. There, jumbled up with the remains of the mulberry-leaves, is a copious mass of droppings, impregnated with the substance which has just so painfully eaten into my skin; there and there only is *lou verin,* as you call it.

It is a relief merely to know the cause of one's trouble; but I will provide you with another consolation. When you remove the litter and renew the leaves, you should raise the irritant dust as little as possible; you should avoid lifting your hands to your face, above all to your eyes; and it is just as well to turn down your sleeves in order to protect your arms. If you take these precautions, you will suffer no unpleasantness.

The successful result obtained with the Silkworm caused me to foresee a similar success with any caterpillar that I might come across. The facts fully confirmed my expectations. I tested the stercoral pellets of various caterpillars, not selected, but just as the hazard of collecting provided them: the Great Tortoiseshell, the Heath Fritillary, the Large Cabbage Butterfly, the Spurge Hawk-moth, the Great Peacock Moth, the Death's-head Moth, the Puss-moth, the Tiger-moth and the Arbu-

An Insect Virus

tus Liparis. All my tests, with not a single exception, brought about stinging, of various degrees of violence, it is true. I attribute these differences in the result to the greater or lesser quantities of the virus employed, for it is impossible to measure the dose.

So the urticating excretion is common to all the caterpillars. By a very unexpected reversion of the usual order of things, the popular repugnance is well-founded; prejudice becomes truth: all caterpillars are venomous. We must draw a distinction, however: with the same venomous properties, some are inoffensive and others, far less numerous, are to be feared. Whence comes this difference?

I note that the caterpillars marked out as stinging live in communities and weave themselves dwellings of silk, in which they stay for long periods. Moreover, they are furry. Of this number are the Pine Processionary, the Oak Processionary and the caterpillars of various Lipares.

Let us consider the first-named in particular. His nest, a voluminous bag spun at the tip of a branch, is magnificent in its silky whiteness, on the outside; inside, it is a disgusting cesspit. The colony remains in it all

The Life of the Caterpillar

day and for the greater part of the night. It sallies forth in procession only in the late hours of twilight, to browse upon the adjacent foliage. This long internment leads to a considerable accumulation of droppings in the heart of the dwelling.

From all the threads of this labyrinth hang chaplets of these droppings; the walls are upholstered with them in all the corridors; the little narrow chambers are encumbered with them. From a nest the size of a man's head I have obtained, with a sieve, over three-quarters of a pint of stercoral pellets.

Now it is in the midst of this ordure that the caterpillars live and have their being; in the midst of it they move, swarm and sleep. The results of this utter contempt for the rules of cleanliness are obvious. Certainly, the Processionary does not soil his coat by contact with those dry pellets; he leaves his home with his costume neat and glossy, suggesting not a suspicion of uncleanliness. No matter: by constantly rubbing against the droppings, his bristles are inevitably smeared with virus and their barbs poisoned. The caterpillar becomes irritant, because his manner of life subjects him to prolonged contact with his own ordure.

Now consider the Hedgehog Caterpillar. Why is he harmless, despite his fierce and hirsute aspect? Because he lives in isolation and is always on the move. His mane, apt though it be to collect and retain irritant particles, will never give us the itch, for the simple reason that the caterpillar does not lie on his excretions. Distributed all over the fields and far from numerous, owing to the caterpillar's solitary habits, the droppings, though poisonous, cannot transfer their properties to a fleece which does not come into contact with them. If the Hedgehog lived in a community, in a nest serving as a cesspit, he would be the foremost of our stinging caterpillars.

At first sight, the barrack-rooms of the Silkworm-nurseries seem to fulfil the conditions necessary to the surface venom of the worms. Each change of litter results in the removal of basketfuls of droppings from the trays. Over this heaped-up ordure the Silkworms swarm. How is it that they do not acquire the poisonous properties of their own excrement?

The Life of the Caterpillar

I see two reasons. In the first place, they are hairless; and a brushlike coat may well be indispensable to the collection of the virus. In the second place, far from lying in the filth, they live above the soiled stratum, being largely separated from it by the bed of leaves, which is renewed several times a day. Despite crowding, the population of a tray has nothing that can be compared with the ordinary habits of the Processionary; and so it remains harmless, in spite of its stercoral toxin.

These first enquiries lead us to conclusions which themselves are very remarkable. All caterpillars excrete an urticating matter, which is identical throughout the series. But, if the poison is to manifest itself and to cause us that characteristic itching, it is indispensable that the caterpillar shall dwell in a community, spending long periods in the nest, a silken bag laden with droppings. These furnish the virus; the caterpillar's hairs collect it and transfer it to us.

The time has come to tackle the problem from another point of view. Is this formidable matter which always accompanies the excretions a digestive residuum? Is it not rather one of those waste substances which the organism engenders while at work, waste substances designated by the general appellation of urinary products?

To isolate these products, to collect them separately, would scarcely be practicable, if we did not have recourse to what follows on the metamorphosis. Every Moth, on emerging from her chrysalis, rejects a copious mixture of uric acid and various humours of which very little is as yet known. It may be compared with the broken plaster of a building rebuilt on a new plan and represents the by-products of the mighty labours accomplished in the transfigured insect. These remains are essentially urinary products, with no admixture of digested foodstuffs.

To what insect shall I apply for this residuum? Chance does many things. I collect, from the old elm-tree in the garden, about a hundred curious caterpillars. They have seven rows of prickles of an amber yellow, a sort of bush with four or five branches. I shall learn from the Butterfly that they belong to the Great Tortoiseshell *(Vanessa polychloros,* LIN.).

Reared on elm-leaves under a wire-gauze cover, my caterpillars undergo their trans-

The Life of the Caterpillar

formation towards the end of May. Their chrysalids are specked with brown on a whitish ground and display on the under surface six radiant silvery spots, a sort of decorative tinsel, like so many mirrors. Fixed by the tail with a silken pad, they hang from the top of the dome, swinging at the least movement and emitting vivid flashes of light from their reflectors. My children are amazed at this living chandelier. It is a treat for them when I allow them to come and admire it in my animal studio.

Another surprise awaits them, this time a tragic one, however. A fortnight later, the Butterflies emerge. I have placed under the cover a large sheet of white paper, which will receive the desired products. I call the children. What do they see on the paper?

Large spots of blood. Under their very eyes, from up there, at the top of the dome, a butterfly lets fall a great red drop: plop! No joy for the children to-day; anxiety rather, almost fear.

I send them away, saying to them:

"Be sure and remember, kiddies, what you have just seen; and, if ever any one talks to you about showers of blood, don't be silly and

An Insect Virus

frightened. A pretty Butterfly is the cause of those blood-red stains, which have been known to terrify country-folk. The moment she is born, she casts out, in the form of a red liquid, the remains of her old caterpillar body, a body remodelled and reborn in a beautiful shape. That is the whole secret."

When my artless visitors have departed, I resume my examination of the rain of blood falling under the cover. Still clinging to the shell of its chrysalis, each Tortoiseshell ejects and sheds upon the paper a great red drop, which, if left standing, deposits a powdery pink sediment, composed of urates. The liquid is now a deep crimson.

When the whole thing is perfectly dry, I cut out of the spotted paper some of the richer stains and steep the bits in ether. The spots on the paper remain as red as at the outset; and the liquid assumes a light lemon tint. When reduced by evaporation to a few drops, this liquid provides me with what I require to soak my square of blotting-paper.

What shall I say to avoid repeating myself? The effects of the new caustic are precisely the same as those which I experienced when I used the droppings of the Processionary. The same itching, the same burning, the same swelling with the flesh throbbing and inflamed, the same serous exudation, the same peeling of the skin, the same persistent redness, which lingers for three or four months, long after the ulceration itself has disappeared.

Without being very painful, the sore is so irksome and above all looks so ugly that I swear never to let myself in for it again. Henceforth, without waiting for the thing to eat into my flesh, I shall remove the caterpillar plaster as soon as I feel a conclusive itching.

In the course of these painful experiences, friends upbraid me with not having recourse to the assistance of some animal, such as the Guinea-pig, that stock victim of the physiologists. I take no note of their reproaches. The animal is a stoic. It says nothing of its sufferings. If, the torture being a little too intense, it complains, I am in no position to interpret its cries exactly or to attribute them to a definite impression.

The Guinea-pig will not say:

"It smarts, it itches, it burns."

He will simply say:

An Insect Virus

"That hurts."

As I want to know the details of the sensations experienced, the best thing is to resort to my own skin, the only witness on whose evidence I can rely implicitly.

At the risk of provoking a smile, I will venture on another confession. As I begin to see into the matter more clearly, I hesitate to torture or destroy a single creature in God's great community. The life of the least of these is a thing to be respected. We can take it away, but we cannot give it. Peace to those innocents, so little interested in our investigations! What does our restless curiosity matter to their calm and sacred ignorance? If we wish to know, let us pay the price ourselves as far as possible. The acquisition of an idea is well worth the sacrifice of a bit of skin.

The Elm Tortoiseshell, with her rain of blood, may leave us to a certain extent in doubt. Might not this strange red substance, with its unusual appearance, contain a poison which is likewise exceptional? I address myself therefore to the Mulberry Bombyx, to the Pine Bombyx and to the Great Peacock.

The Life of the Caterpillar

I collect the uric excretions ejected by the newly hatched Moths.

This time, the liquid is whitish, sullied here and there with uncertain tints. There is no blood-red colouration; but the result is the same. The virulent energy manifests itself in the most definite manner. Therefore the Processionary's virus exists equally in all caterpillars, in all Butterflies and Moths emerging from the chrysalis; and this virus is a by-product of the organism, a urinary product.

The curiosity of our minds is insatiable. The moment a reply is obtained, a fresh question arises. Why should the Lepidoptera alone be endowed in this manner? The organic labours accomplished within them cannot differ greatly, as to the nature of the materials, from those presiding over the maintenance of life in other insects. Therefore these others also elaborate a by-product which has stinging powers. This can be verified—and that forthwith—with the elements at my disposal.

The first reply is furnished by *Cetonia floricola,* of which Beetle I collect half a dozen chrysalids from a heap of leaves half-converted into mould. A box receives my find, laid on a sheet of white paper, on which the urinary fluid of the perfect insect will fall as soon as the caskets are broken.

The weather is favourable and I have not long to wait. The thing is done: the matter rejected is white, the usual colour of these residua, in the great majority of insects, at the moment of the metamorphosis. Though by no means abundant, it nevertheless provokes on my fore-arm a violent itching, together with mortification of the skin, which comes off in flakes. The reason why it does not display a more distinct sore is that I judged it prudent to end the experiment. The burning and itching tell me enough as to the results of a contact unduly prolonged.

Now to the Hymenoptera. I have not in my possession, I regret to say, any of those with whom my rearing-chambers used formerly to provide me, whether Honey-bee or Hunting Wasps. I have only a Green Saw-fly, whose larva lives in numerous families on the leaves of the alder. Reared under cover, this larva provides me with enough tiny black droppings to fill a thimble. That is sufficient: the urtication is quite definite.

I take next the insects with incomplete

The Life of the Caterpillar

transformations. My recent rearings have given me quite a collection of excretions emanating from the Orthoptera. I consult those of the Vine Ephippiger[1] and the Great Grey Locust. Both sting to a degree which once more makes me regret my lavish hand.

We will be satisfied with this; indeed my arms demand as much, for, tattooed with red squares, they refuse to make room for fresh brandings. The examples are sufficiently varied to impose the following conclusion: the Processionary's virus is found in a host of other insects, apparently even in the entire series. It is a urinary product inherent in the entomological organism.

The dejections of insects, especially those evacuated at the end of the metamorphosis, contain or are even almost entirely composed of urates. Can the stinging material be the inevitable associate of uric acid? It should then form part of the excrement of the bird and the reptile, which in both cases is very rich in urates. Here again is a suspicion worthy of verification by experiment.

For the moment it is impossible for me to question the reptile; it is easy, on the other

[1] A species of Grasshopper.—*Translator's Note.*

An Insect Virus

hand, to interrogate the bird, whose reply will suffice. I accept what is offered by chance: an insectivorous bird, the Swallow, and a graminivorous bird, the Goldfinch. Well, their urinary dejections, when carefully separated from the digestive residua, have not the slightest stinging effect. The virus that causes itching is independent therefore of uric acid. It accompanies it in the insect class, without being its invariable concomitant every elsewhere.

A last step remains for us to take, namely, to isolate the stinging element and to obtain it in quantities permitting of precise enquiries into its nature and properties. It seems to me that medical science might turn to account a material whose energy rivals that of cantharides, if it does not exceed it. The question appeals to me. I would gladly return to my beloved chemistry; but I should want reagents, apparatus, a laboratory, a whole costly arsenal of which I must not dream, afflicted as I am with a terrible ailment: impecuniosity, the searcher's habitual lot.

CHAPTER IX

THE PSYCHES: THE LAYING

IN THE springtime, old walls and dusty
roads harbour a surprise for whoso has
eyes to see. Tiny faggots, for no apparent
reason, set themselves in motion and make
their way along by sudden jerks. The inani-
mate comes to life, the immovable stirs. How
does this come about? Look closer and the
motive power will stand revealed.

Enclosed within the moving bundle is a
fairly well-developed caterpillar, prettily
striped in black and white. Seeking for food
or perhaps for a spot where the transformation can be effected, he hurries along timidly,
attired in a queer rig-out of twigs from which
nothing emerges except the head and the front
part of the body, which is furnished with six
short legs. At the least alarm he goes right
in and does not budge again. This is the
whole secret of the little roaming bundle of
sticks.

The faggot caterpillar belongs to the
Psyche group, whose name conveys an allu-

sion to the classic Psyche, symbolical of the soul. We must not allow this phrase to carry our thoughts to loftier heights than is fitting. The nomenclator, with his rather circumscribed view of the world, did not trouble about the soul when inventing his descriptive label. He simply wanted a pretty name; and certainly he could have hit on nothing better.

To protect himself from the weather, our chilly, bare-skinned Psyche builds himself a portable shelter, a travelling cottage which the owner never leaves until he becomes a Moth. It is something better than a hut on wheels with a thatched roof to it: it is a hermit's frock, made of an unusual sort of frieze. In the valley of the Danube the peasant wears a goatskin cloak fastened with a belt of rushes. The Psyche dons an even more rustic apparel. He makes himself a suit of clothes out of hop-poles. It is true that, beneath this rude conglomeration, which would be a regular hair-shirt to a skin as delicate as his, he puts a thick lining of silk. The Clythra Beetle garbs himself in pottery; this one dresses himself in a faggot.

In April, on the walls of my chief observa-

The Life of the Caterpillar

tory, that famous pebbly acre with its wealth of insect life, I find the Psyche who is to furnish me with my most circumstantial and detailed records.[1] He is at this period in the torpor of the approaching metamorphosis. As we can ask him nothing else for the moment, let us look into the construction and composition of his faggot.

It is a not irregular structure, spindle-shaped and about an inch and a half long. The pieces that compose it are fixed in front and free at the back, are arranged anyhow and would form a rather ineffective shelter against the sun and rain if the recluse had no other protection than his thatched roof.

The word thatch is suggested to my mind by a summary inspection of what I see, but it is not an exact expression in this case. On the contrary, graminaceous straws are rare, to the great advantage of the future family, which, as we shall learn presently, would find nothing to suit them in jointed planks. What predominates is remnants of very small stalks, light, soft and rich in pith, such as are possessed by various Chicoriaceæ. I recognize in

[1] *Psyche unicolor,* HUFN.; *P. graminella,* SCHIFFER-MÜLLER.—*Author's Note.*

188

The Psyches: the Laying

particular the floral stems of the mouse-ear
hawkweed and the Nimes pterotheca. Next
come bits of grass-leaves, scaly twigs provided
by the cypress-tree and all sorts of little sticks,
coarse materials adopted for the lack of anything better. Lastly, if the favourite cylindrical pieces fall short, the mantle is sometimes finished off with an ample flounced tippet, that is to say, with fragments of dry
leaves of any kind.

Incomplete as it is, this list shows us that
the caterpillar apart from his preference for
pithy morsels, has no very exclusive tastes.
He employs indifferently anything that he
comes upon, provided that it be light, very
dry, softened by long exposure to the air and
of suitable dimensions. All his finds, if they
come anywhere near his estimates, are used
just as they are, without any alterations or
sawing to reduce them to the proper length.
The Psyche does not trim the laths that go
to form his roof; he gathers them as he finds
them. His work is limited to imbricating
them one after the other by fixing them at the
fore-end.

In order to lend itself to the movements of
the journeying caterpillar and in particular to

The Life of the Caterpillar

facilitate the action of the head and legs when a new piece is to be placed in position, the front part of the sheath requires a special structure. Here a casing of beams is no longer allowable, for their length and stiffness would hamper the artisan and even make his work impossible; what is essential here is a flexible neck, able to bend in all directions. The assemblage of stakes does, in fact, end suddenly at some distance from the fore-part and is there replaced by a collar in which the silken woof is merely hardened with very tiny ligneous particles, tending to strengthen the material without impairing its flexibility. This collar, which gives free movement, is so important that all the Psyches make equal use of it, however much the rest of the work may differ. All carry, in front of the faggot of sticks, a yielding neck, soft to the touch, formed inside of a web of pure silk and velveted outside with a fine sawdust which the caterpillar obtains by crushing with his mandibles any sort of dry straw.

A similar velvet, but lustreless and faded, apparently through age, finishes the sheath at the back, in the form of a rather long, bare appendix, open at the end.

The Psyches: the Laying

Let us now remove the outside of the straw envelope, shredding it piecemeal. The demolition gives us a varying number of joists: I have counted as many as eighty and more. The ruin that remains is a cylindrical sheath wherein we discover, from one end to the other, the structure which we perceived at the front and rear, the two parts which are naturally bare. The tissue everywhere is of very stout silk, which resists without breaking when pulled by the fingers, a smooth tissue, beautifully white inside, drab and wrinkled outside, where it bristles with encrusted woody particles.

There will be an opportunity later to discover by what means the caterpillar makes himself so complicated a garment, in which are laid one upon the other, in a definite order, first, the extremely fine satin which is in direct contact with the skin; next, the mixed stuff, a sort of frieze dusted with ligneous matter, which saves the silk and gives consistency to the work; lastly, the surtout of overlapping laths.

While retaining this general threefold arrangement, the scabbard offers notable variations of structural detail in the different

species. Here, for instance, is a second
Psyche,[1] the most belated of the three which
I have chanced to come upon. I meet him
towards the end of June, hurrying across
some dusty path near the houses. His cases
surpass those of the previous species both in
size and in regularity of arrangement. They
form a thick coverlet, of many pieces, in which
I recognize here fragments of hollow stalks,
there bits of fine straw, with perhaps straps
formed of blades of grass. In front there
is never any mantilla of dead leaves, a troublesome piece of finery which, without being in
regular use, is pretty frequent in the costume
of the first-named species. At the back, no
long, denuded vestibule. Save for the indispensable collar at the aperture, all the rest
is cased in logs. There is not much variety
about the thing, but, when all is said, there
is a certain elegance in its stern faultlessness.

The smallest in size and simplest in dress
is the third,[2] who is very common at the end
of winter on the walls, as well as in the fur-
rows of the barks of gnarled old trees, be they

[1] As far as can be judged from the case only, *Psyche
. febretta*, BOYER DE FONSCOLOMBE.—*Author's Note.*

[2] *Fumea comitella* and *F. intermediella*, BRUAND.—*Author's Note.*

192

The Psyches: the Laying

olive-trees, holm-oaks, elms or almost any
other. His case, a modest little bundle, is
hardly more than two-fifths of an inch in
length. A dozen rotten straws, gleaned at
random and fixed close to one another in a
parallel direction, represent, with the silk
sheath, his whole outlay on dress. It would
be difficult to clothe one's self more eco-
nomically.

This pigmy, apparently so uninteresting,
shall supply us with our first records of the
curious life-story of the Psyches. I gather
him in profusion in April and instal him in
a wire bell-jar. What he eats I know not.
My ignorance would be grievous under other
conditions; but at present I need not trouble
about provisions. Taken from their walls
and trees, where they had suspended themselves for their transformation, most of my
little Psyches are in the chrysalis state. A
few of them are still active. They hasten to
clamber to the top of the trellis-work; they
fix themselves there perpendicularly by means
of a little silk cushion; then everything is still.

June comes to an end; and the male Moths
are hatched, leaving the chrysalid wrapper
half caught in the case, which remains fixed

where it is and will remain there indefinitely until dismantled by the weather. The emergence is effected through the hinder end of the bundle of sticks, the only way by which it can be effected. Having permanently closed the top opening, the real door of the house, by fastening it to the support which he has chosen, the caterpillar therefore has turned the other way round and undergone his transformation in a reversed position, which enables the adult insect to emerge through the outlet made at the back, the only one now free.

For that matter, this is the method followed by all the Psyches. The case has two apertures. The front one, which is more regular and more carefully constructed, is at the caterpillar's service so long as larval activity lasts. It is closed and firmly fastened to its support at the time of the nymphosis. The hinder one, which is faulty and even hidden by the sagging of the sides, is at the Moth's service. It does not really open until right at the end, when pushed by the chrysalis or the adult insect.

In their modest pearl-grey dress, with their insignificant wing-equipment, hardly exceeding that of a Common Fly, our little Moths are still not without elegance. They have handsome feathery plumes for antennæ; their wings are edged with delicate fringes. They whirl very fussily inside the bell-jar; they skim the ground, fluttering their wings; they crowd eagerly around certain sheaths which nothing on the outside distinguishes from the others. They alight upon them and sound them with their plumes.

This feverish agitation marks them as lovers in search of their brides. This one here, that one there, each of them finds his mate. But the coy one does not leave her home. Things happen very discreetly through the wicket left open at the free end of the case. The male stands on the threshold of this back-door for a little while; and then it is over: the wedding is finished. There is no need for us to linger over these nuptials in which the parties concerned do not know, do not see each other.

I hasten to place in a glass tube the few cases in which the mysterious events have happened. Some days later, the recluse comes out of the sheath and shows herself in all her wretchedness. Call that little fright a Moth!

The Life of the Caterpillar

One cannot easily get used to the idea of such poverty. The caterpillar of the start was no humbler-looking. There are no wings, none at all; no silky fur either. At the tip of the abdomen, a round, tufty pad, a crown of dirty-white velvet; on each segment, in the middle of the back, a large rectangular dark patch: these are the sole attempts at ornament. The mother Psyche renounces all the beauty which her name of Moth promised.

From the centre of the hairy coronet a long ovipositor stands out, consisting of two parts, one stiff, forming the base of the implement, the other soft and flexible, sheathed in the first just as a telescope fits in its tube. The laying mother bends herself into a hook, grips the lower end of her case with her six feet and drives her probe into the back-window, a window which serves manifold purposes, allowing of the consummation of the clandestine marriage, the emergence of the fertilized bride, the installation of the eggs and, lastly, the exodus of the young family.

There, at the free end of her case, the mother remains for a long time, bowed and motionless. What can she be doing in this contemplative attitude? She is lodging her

196

eggs in the house which she has just left; she
is bequeathing the maternal cottage to her
heirs. Some thirty hours pass and the ovipositor is at last withdrawn. The laying is
finished.

A little wadding, supplied by the coronet
on the hind-quarters, closes the door and al-
lays the dangers of invasion. The fond
mother makes a barricade for her brood of
the sole ornament which, in her extreme in-
digence, she possesses. Better still, she makes
a rampart of her body. Bracing herself convulsively on the threshold of her home, she
dies there, dries up there, devoted to her
family even after death. It needs an accident,
a breath of air, to make her fall from her
post.

Let us now open the case. It contains the
chrysalid wrapper, intact except for the front
breach through which the Psyche emerged.
The male, because of his wings and his
plumes, very cumbersome articles when he is
about to make his way through the narrow
pass, takes advantage of his chrysalis state
to make a start for the door and come out
half-way. Then, bursting his amber tunic,
the delicate Moth finds an open space, where

197

The Life of the Caterpillar

flight is possible, right in front of him. The mother, unprovided with wings and plumes, is not compelled to observe any such precautions. Her cylindrical form, bare and differing but little from that of the caterpillar, allows her to crawl, to slip into the narrow passage and to come forth without obstacle. Her cast chrysalid skin is, therefore, left right at the back of the case, well covered by the thatched roof.

And this is an act of prudence marked by exquisite tenderness. The eggs, in fact, are packed in the barrel, in the parchmentlike wallet formed by the slough. The mother has thrust her telescopic ovipositor to the bottom of that receptacle and has methodically gone on laying until it is full. Not satisfied with bequeathing her home and her velvet coronet to her offspring, as a last sacrifice she leaves them her skin.

With a view to observing at my ease the events which are soon to happen, I extract one of these chrysalid bags, stuffed with eggs, from its faggot and place it by itself, beside its case, in a glass tube. I have not long to wait. In the first week of July, I find myself all of a sudden in possession of a large family.

The Psyches: the Laying

The quickness of the hatching balked my watchfulness. The new-born caterpillars, about forty in number, have already had time to garb themselves.

They wear a Persian head-dress, a mage's tiara in dazzling white plush. Or, to abandon high-flown language, let us say a cotton night-cap without a tassel; only the cap does not stand up from the head: it covers the hind-quarters. Great animation reigns in the tube, which is a spacious residence for such vermin. They roam about gaily, with their caps sticking up almost perpendicular to the floor. With a tiara like that and things to eat, life must be sweet indeed.

But what do they eat? I try a little of everything that grows on the bare stone and the gnarled old trees. Nothing is welcomed. More eager to dress than to feed themselves, the Psyches scorn what I set before them. My ignorance as an insect-breeder will not matter, provided that I succeed in seeing with what materials and in what manner the first outlines of the cap are woven.

I may fairly hope to achieve this ambition, as the chrysalid bag is far from having exhausted its contents. I find in it, teeming

The Life of the Caterpillar

amid the rumpled wrapper of the eggs, an additional family as numerous as the swarm that is already out. The total laying must therefore amount to five or six dozen. I transfer to another receptacle the precocious band which is already dressed and keep only the naked laggards in the tube. They have bright red heads, with the rest of their bodies dirty white; and they measure hardly a twenty-fifth of an inch in length.

My patience is not long put to the test. Next day, little by little, singly or in groups, the belated grubs quit the chrysalid bag. They come out without breaking the frail wallet, through the front breach made by the liberation of the mother. Not one of them utilizes it as a dress-material, though it has the delicacy and amber colouring of an onion-skin; nor do any of them make use of a fine quilting which lines the inside of the bag and forms an exquisitely soft bed for the eggs. This down, whose origin we shall have to investigate presently, ought, one would say, to make an excellent blanket for these chilly ones, impatient to cover themselves up. Not a single one uses it; there would not be enough to go round.

The Psyches: the Laying

All go straight to the coarse faggot, which
I left in contact with the wallet that was the
chrysalis. Time presses. Before making
your entrance into the world and going
agrazing, you must first be clad. All therefore, with equal fury, attack the old sheath
and hastily dress themselves in the mother's
cast clothes. Some turn their attention to bits
that happen to be open lengthwise and scrape
the soft, white inner layer; others, greatly
daring, penetrate into the tunnel of a hollow
stalk and go and collect their cotton goods
in the dark. At such times the materials are
first-class; and the garment woven is of a
dazzling white. Others bite deep into the
piece which they select and make themselves
a motley garment, in which dark-coloured
particles mar the snowy whiteness of the rest.

The tool which they use for their gleaning
consists of the mandibles, shaped like wide
shears with five strong teeth apiece. The two
planes fit into each other and form an implement capable of seizing and slicing any
fibre, however small. Seen under the microscope, it is a wonderful specimen of mechanical precision and power. Were the Sheep
similarly equipped in proportion to her size,

she would browse upon the bottom of the trees instead of cropping the grass.

A very instructive workshop is that of the Psyche-vermin toiling to make themselves a cotton night-cap. There are numbers of things to remark in both the finish of the work and the ingenuity of the methods employed. To avoid repeating ourselves, we will say nothing about these yet, but wait for a little and return to the subject when setting forth the talents of a second Psyche, of larger stature and easier to observe. The two weavers observe exactly the same procedure.

Nevertheless let us take a glance at the bottom of the egg-cup, a general workyard in which I instal my dwarfs as the cases turn them out. There are some hundreds of them, with the sheaths from which they came and an assortment of clipped stalks, chosen from among the driest and richest in pith. What a whirl! What bewildering animation!

In order to see man, Micromégas cut himself a lens out of a diamond of his necklace; he held his breath lest the storm from his nostrils should blow the mite away. I in my turn will be the good giant, newly arriving from Sirius; I screw a magnifying-glass into my eye and am careful not to breathe for fear of overturning and sweeping out of existence my cotton-workers. If I need one of them, to focus him under a stronger glass, I lime him as it were, seizing him with the fine point of a needle which I have passed over my lips. Taken away from his work, the tiny caterpillar struggles at the end of the needle, shrivels up, makes himself, small as he is, still smaller; he strives to withdraw as far as possible into his clothing, which as yet is incomplete, the merest flannel vest or even a narrow scarf, covering nothing but the top of his shoulders. Let us leave him to complete his coat. I give a puff; and the creature is swallowed up in the crater of the egg-cup.

And this speck is alive. It is industrious; it is versed in the art of blanket-making. An orphan, born that moment, it knows how to cut itself out of its dead mother's old clothes the wherewithal to clothe itself in its turn. Soon it will become a carpenter, an assembler of timber, to make a defensive covering for its delicate fabric. What must instinct be, to be capable of awakening such industries in an atom!

It is at the end of June also that I obtain,

The Life of the Caterpillar

in his adult shape, the Psyche whose scabbard is continued underneath by a long, naked vestibule. Most of the cases are fastened by a silk pad to the trelliswork of the cage and hang vertically, like stalactites. Some few of them have never left the ground. Half immersed in the sand, they stand erect, with their rear in the air and their fore-part buried and firmly anchored to the side of the pan by means of a silky paste.

This inverted position excludes any idea of weight as a guide in the caterpillar's preparations. An adept at turning round in his cabin, he is careful, before he sinks into the immobility of pupadom, to turn his head now upwards, now downwards, towards the opening, so that the adult insect, which is much less free than the larva in its movements, may reach the outside without obstacle.

Moreover, it is the pupa itself, the unbending chrysalis, incapable of turning and obliged to move all in one piece, which, stubbornly crawling, carries the male to the threshold of the case. It emerges half way at the end of the uncovered silky vestibule and there breaks, obstructing the opening with its slough as it does so. For a time the

The Psyches: the Laying

Moth stands still on the roof of the cottage, allowing his humours to evaporate, his wings to spread and gather strength; then at last the gallant takes flight, in search of her for whose sake he has made himself so spruce.

He wears a costume of deepest black, all except the edges of the wings, which, having no scales, remain diaphanous. His antennæ, likewise black, are wide and graceful plumes. Were they on a larger scale, they would throw the feathered beauty of the Marabou and Ostrich into the shade. The bravely be-plumed one visits case after case in his tortuous flight, prying into the secrets of those alcoves. If things go as he wishes, he settles, with a quick flutter of his wings, on the extremity of the denuded vestibule. Comes the wedding, as discreet as that of the smaller Psyche. Here is yet another who does not see or at most catches a fleeting glimpse of her for whose sake he has donned Marabou-feathers and a black-velvet cloak.

The recluse on her side is equally impatient. The lovers are short-lived; they die in my cages within three or four days, so that, for long intervals, until the hatching of some late-comer, the female population is

The Life of the Caterpillar

short of suitors. So, when the morning sun,
already hot, strikes the cage, a very singular
spectacle is repeated many times before my
eyes. The entrance to the vestibule swells
imperceptibly, opens and emits a mass of in-
finitely delicate down. A Spider's web,
carded and made into wadding, would give
nothing of such gossamer fineness. It is a
vaporous cloud. Then, from out of this incomparable eiderdown, appear the head and
fore-part of a very different sort of caterpillar from the original collector of straws.

It is the mistress of the house, the marriageable Moth, who, feeling her hour about
to come and failing to receive the expected
visit, herself makes the advances and goes, as
far as she can, to meet her plumed swain.
He does not come hastening up and for good
reason: there is not a male left in the establishment. For two or three hours the poor
forsaken one leans, without moving, from her
window. Then, tired of waiting, very gently
she goes indoors again, backwards, and returns to her cell.

Next day, the day after and later still, as
long as her strength permits, she reappears
on her balcony, always in the morning, in the

The Psyches: the Laying

soft rays of a warm sun and always on a sofa
of that incomparable down, which disperses
and turns to vapour if I merely fan it with
my hand. Again no one comes. For the last
time the disappointed Moth goes back to her
boudoir, never to leave it again. She dies
in it, dries up, a useless thing. I hold my bell-
jars responsible for this crime against motherhood. In the open fields, without a doubt,
sooner or later wooers would have appeared,
coming from the four winds.

The said bell-jars have an even more pitiful catastrophe on their conscience. Sometimes, leaning too far from her window, mis-
calculating the balance between the front of
the body, which is at liberty, and the back,
which remains sheathed in its case, the Moth
allows herself to drop to the ground. It is
all up now with the fallen one and her lineage.
Still, there is one good thing about it. Acci-
dents such as this lay bare the mother Psyche,
without our having to break into her house.

What a miserable creature she is, a great
deal uglier than the original caterpillar!
Here transfiguration spells disfigurement,
progress means retrogression. What we have
before our eyes is a wrinkled satchel, an

earthy-yellow sausage; and this horror, worse than a maggot, is a Moth in the full bloom of life, a genuine adult Moth. She is the betrothed of the elegant black Bombyx, all plumed with Marabou-feathers, and represents to him the last word in beauty. As the proverb says, beauty lies in lovers' eyes: a profound truth which the Psyche confirms in striking fashion.

Let us describe the ugly little sausage. A very small head, a paltry globule, disappearing almost entirely in the folds of the first segment. What need is there of cranium and brains for a germ-bag! And so the tiny creature almost does without them, reduces them to the simplest expression. Nevertheless, there are two black ocular specks. Do these vestigial eyes see their way about? Not very clearly, we may be sure. The pleasures of light must be very small for this stay-at-home, who appears at her window only on rare occasions, when the male Moth is late in arriving.

The legs are well-shaped, but so short and weak that they are of no use at all for locomotion. The whole body is a pale yellow, semitransparent in front, opaque and stuffed

with eggs behind. Underneath the first segments is a sort of neck-band, that is to say,
a dark stain, the vestige of a crop showing
through the skin. A pad of short down ends
the oviferous part at the back. It is all that
remains of a fleece, of a thin velvet which
the insect rubs off as it moves backwards and
forwards in its narrow lodging. This forms
the flaky mass which whitens the trysting-
window at the wedding-time and also lines
the inside of the sheath with down. In
short, the creature is little more than a bag
swollen with eggs for the best part of its
length. I know nothing lower in the scale of
wretchedness.

The germ-bag moves, but not, of course,
with those vestiges of legs which form too
short and feeble supports; it gets about in a
way that allows it to progress on its back,
belly or side indifferently. A groove is hollowed out at the hinder end of the bag, a
deep, dividing groove which cuts the insect
into two. It runs to the front part, spreading
like a wave, and gently and slowly reaches
the head. This undulation constitutes a step.
When it is done, the animal has advanced
about a twenty-fifth part of an inch.

The Life of the Caterpillar

To go from one end to the other of a box two inches long and filled with fine sand, the living sausage takes nearly an hour. It is by crawling like this that it moves about in its case, when it comes to the threshold to meet its visitor and goes in again.

For three or four days, exposed to the roughness of the soil, the oviferous bag leads a wretched life, creeping about at random, or, more often, standing still. No Moth pays attention to the poor thing, who possesses no attractions outside her home; the lovers pass by with an indifferent air. This coolness is logical enough. Why should she become a mother, if her family is to be abandoned to the inclemencies of the public way? And so, after falling by accident from her case, which would have been the cradle of the youngsters, the wanderer withers in a few days and dies childless.

The fertilized ones—and these are the more numerous—the prudent ones who have saved themselves from a fall by being less lavish with their appearances at the window, reenter the sheath and do not show themselves again once the Moth's visit to the threshold is over. Let us wait a fortnight

The Psyches: the Laying

and then open the case lengthwise with our scissors. At the end, in the widest part, opposite the vestibule, is the slough of the chrysalis, a long, fragile, amber-coloured sack, open at the end that contains the head, the end facing the exit-passage. In this sack, which she fills like a mould, lies the mother, the egg-bladder, now giving no sign of life.

From this amber sheath, which presents all the usual characteristics of a chrysalis, the adult Psyche emerged, in the guise of a shapeless Moth, looking like a big maggot; at the present time, she has slipped back into her old jacket, moulding herself into it in such a way that it becomes difficult to separate the container from the contents. One would take the whole thing for a single body.

It seems very likely that this cast skin, which occupies the best place in the home, formed the Psyche's refuge when, weary of waiting on the threshold of her hall, she retired to the back room. She has therefore gone in and out repeatedly. This constant going and coming, this continual rubbing against the sides of a narrow corridor, just wide enough for her to pass through, ended by stripping her of her down. She had a fleece to start with, a very light and scanty fleece, it is true, but still a vestige of the costume which Moths are wont to wear. This fluff she has lost. What has she done with it?

The Eider robs herself of her down to make a luxurious bed for her brood; the new-born Rabbits lie on a mattress which their mother cards for them with the softest part of her fur, shorn from the belly and neck, wherever the shears of her front teeth can reach it. This fond tenderness is shared by the Psyche, as you will see.

In front of the chrysalid bag is an abundant mass of extra-fine wadding, similar to that of which a few flocks used to fall outside on the occasions when the recluse went to her window. Is it silk? Is it spun muslin? No; but it is something of incomparable delicacy. The microscope recognizes it as the scaly dust, the impalpable down in which every Moth is clad. To give a snug shelter to the little caterpillars who will soon be swarming in the case, to provide them with a refuge in which they can play about and gather strength before entering the wide

The Psyches: the Laying

world, the Psyche has stripped herself of her fur like the mother Rabbit.

This denudation may be a mere mechanical result, an unintentional effect of repeated rubbing against the low-roofed walls; but there is nothing to tell us so. Maternity has its foresight, even among the humblest. I therefore picture the hairy Moth twisting about, going to and fro in the narrow passage in order to get rid of the fleece and prepare bedding for her offspring. It is even possible that she manages to use her lips, that vestige of a mouth, in order to pull out the down that refuses to come away of itself.

No matter what the method of shearing may be, a mound of scales and hairs fills up the case in front of the chrysalid bag. For the moment, it is a barricade preventing access to the house, which is open at the hinder end; soon, it will be a downy couch on which the little caterpillars will rest for a while after leaving the egg. Here, warmly ensconced in a rug of extreme softness, they call a halt as a preparation for the emergence and the work that follows it.

Not that silk is lacking: on the contrary, it abounds. The caterpillar lavished it du-

The Life of the Caterpillar

ring his time as a spinner and a picker-up of
straws. The whole interior of the case is
padded with thick white satin. But how
greatly preferable to this too-compact and
luxurious upholstery is the delightful eiderdown bedding of the new-born youngsters!

We know the preparations made for the
coming family. Now, where are the eggs?
At what spot are they laid? The smallest
of my three Psyches, who is less misshapen
than the others and freer in her movements,
leaves her case altogether. She possesses a
long ovipositor and inserts it, through the
exit-hole, right into the chrysalid slough,
which is left where it was in the form of a
bag. This slough receives the laying. When
the operation is finished and the bag of eggs
is full, the mother dies outside, hanging on to
the case.

The two other Psyches, who do not carry
telescopic ovipositors and whose only method
of changing their position is a dubious sort
of crawling, have more singular customs to
show us. One might quote with regard to
them what used to be said of the Roman
matrons, those model mothers:

"Domi mansit, lanam fecit."

214

The Psyches: the Laying

Yes, *lanam fecit*. The Psyche does not really work the wool on the distaff; but at least she bequeathes to her sons her own fleece converted into a heap of wadding. Yes, *domi mansit*. She never leaves her house, not even for her wedding, not even for the purpose of laying her eggs.

We have seen how, after receiving the visit of the male, the shapeless Moth, that uncouth sausage, retreats to the back of her case and withdraws into her chrysalid slough, which she fills exactly, just as though she had never left it. The eggs are in their place then and there; they occupy the regulation sack favoured by the various Psyches. Of what use would a laying be now? Strictly speaking, there is none, in fact; that is to say, the eggs do not leave the mother's womb. The living pouch which has engendered them keeps them within itself.

Soon this bag loses its moisture by evaporation; it dries up and at the same time remains sticking to the chrysalid wrapper, that firm support. Let us open the thing. What does the magnifying-glass show us? A few trachean threads, lean bundles of muscles, nervous ramifications, in short, the relics of

The Life of the Caterpillar

a form of vitality reduced to its simplest expression. Taken all around, very nearly nothing. The rest of the contents is a mass of eggs, an agglomeration of germs numbering close upon three hundred. In a word, the insect is one enormous ovary, assisted by just so much as enables it to perform its functions.

CHAPTER X

THE PSYCHES: THE CASES

THE hatching of the eggs takes place in the first fortnight of July. The little grubs measure about one twenty-fifth of an inch. Their head and the upper part of the first thoracic segment are a glossy black, the next two segments brownish and the rest of the body a pale amber. Sharp, lively little creatures, who run about with short, quick steps, they swarm all over the spongy, hairy tissue resulting from the cast-off clothing of the eggs.

The books tell me that the little Psyches begin by eating up their mother: a loathsome banquet for which the said books must accept responsibility. I see nothing of the sort; and I do not even understand how the idea arose. The mother bequeaths to her sons her case, whose straws are searched for wadding, the material of the first coat; out of her chrysalid slough and her skin she makes them a two-fold shelter for the hatching-time; with

The Life of the Caterpillar

her down she prepares a defensive barricade for them and a place wherein to wait before emerging. Thus all is given, all spent with a view to the future. Save for some thin, dry strips which my lens can only with difficulty distinguish, there is nothing left that could provide a cannibal feast for so numerous a family.

No, my little Psyches, you do not eat your mother. In vain do I watch you: never, either to clothe or to feed himself, does any one of you lay a tooth upon the remains of the deceased. The maternal skin is left untouched, as are those other insignificant relics, the layer of muscular tissue and the network of air-ducts. The sack left behind by the chrysalis also remains intact.

The time comes to quit the natal wallet. An outlet has been contrived long beforehand, saving the youngsters from committing any act of violence against what was once their mother. There is no sacrilegious cutting to be done with the shears; the door opens of itself.

When she was a wriggling speck of sausage, the mother's front segments were remarkably translucent, forming a contrast with

the rest of the body. This was very probably a sign of a less dense and less tough
texture than elsewhere. The sign is not mis-
leading. The dry gourd to which the mother
is now reduced has for a neck those diaphanous rings, which, as they withered, became
extremely fragile. Does this neck, this oper-
culum fall of its own accord, or is it pushed
off by the pigmies impatient to get away?
I do not know for certain. This, however,
I can say, that blowing on it is enough to
make it drop off.

In anticipation therefore of the emergence,
an exceedingly easy and perhaps even spontaneous method of decapitation is prepared in
the mother's lifetime. To manufacture a
delicate neck for yourself so that you may be
easily beheaded at the proper time and thus
leave the way free to the youngsters is an
act of devotion in which the most unconscious
maternal affection stands sublimely revealed.
That miserable maggot, that sausage Moth,
scarce able to crawl and yet so clear-sighted
where the future is concerned, staggers the
mind of any one who knows how to think.

The brood emerge from the natal wallet
through the window just opened by the fall of

The Life of the Caterpillar

the head. The chrysalid sack, the second wrapper, presents no obstacle; it has remained open since the adult Psyche left it. Next comes the mass of eiderdown, the heap of fluff of which the mother stripped herself. Here the little caterpillars stop. Much more spaciously and comfortably lodged than in the bag whence they have come, some take a rest, others bustle about, exercise themselves in walking. All pick up strength in preparation for their exodus into the daylight.

They do not stay long amid this luxury. Gradually, as they gain vigour, they come out and spread over the surface of the case. Work begins at once, a very urgent work, that of the wardrobe. The first mouthfuls will come afterwards, when we are dressed.

Montaigne, when putting on the cloak which his father had worn before him, used a touching expression. He said:

"I dress myself in my father."

The young Psyches in the same way dress themselves in their mother: they cover themselves with the clothes left behind by the deceased, they scrape from it the wherewithal to make themselves a cotton frock. The material employed is the pith of the little stalks,

The Psyches: the Cases

especially of the pieces which, split lengthwise, are more easily stripped of their contents. The grub first finds a spot to suit it.
Having done so, it gleans, it planes with its
mandibles. Thus a superbly white wadding
is extracted from old logs.

The manner of beginning the garment is
worth noting. The tiny creature employs as
judicious a method as any which our own industry could hope to discover. The wadding
is collected in infinitesimal pellets. How are
these little particles to be fixed as and when
they are detached by the shears of the mandibles? The manufacturer needs a support,
a base; and this support cannot be obtained
on the caterpillar's own body, for any adher-
ence would be seriously embarrassing and
would hamper freedom of movement. The
difficulty is overcome very cleverly. Scraps
of plush are gathered and by degrees fastened
to one another with threads of silk. This
forms a sort of rectilinear garland in which
the particles collected swing from a common
rope. When these preparations are deemed
sufficient, the little creature passes the garland
round its waist, at about the third segment of
the thorax, so as to leave its six legs free;

then it ties the two ends with a bit of silk.
The result is a girdle, generally incomplete,
but soon completed with other scraps fastened to the silk ribbon that carries everything.

This girdle is the base of the work, the
support. Henceforth, to lengthen the piece,
to enlarge it into the perfect garment, the
grub has only to fix, always at the fore-
edge, with the aid of its spinnerets, now at
the top, now at the bottom or side, the scraps
of pith which the mandibles never cease ex-
tracting. Nothing could be better thought
out than this initial garland laid out flat and
then buckled like a belt around the loins.

Once this base is laid, the weaving-loom
is in full swing. The piece woven is first a
tiny string around the waist; next, by the addition of fresh pellets, always at the fore-
edge, it grows into a scarf, a waistcoat, a
short jacket and lastly a sack, which gradually makes its way backwards, not of itself,
but through the action of the weaver, who
slips forward in the part of the case already
made. In a few hours, the garment is completed. It is by that time a conical hood, a
cloak of magnificent whiteness and finish.

222

The Psyches: the Cases

We now know all about it. On leaving
the maternal hut, without searching, without
distant expeditions which would be so dangerous at that age, the little Psyche finds in the
tender beams of the roof the wherewithal to
clothe himself. He is spared the perils of
roaming in a state of nudity. When he leaves
the house, he will be quite warm, thanks to
the mother, who takes care to instal her
family in the old case and gives it choice materials to work with.

If the grub-worm were to drop out of the
hovel, if some gust of wind swept him to a
distance, most often the poor mite would be
lost. Ligneous straws, rich in pith, dry and
retted to a turn, are not to be found everywhere. It would mean the impossibility of
any clothing and, in that dire poverty, an
early death. But, if suitable materials are
encountered, equal in quality to those be-
queathed by the mother, how is it that the
exile is unable to make use of them? Let us
look into this.

I segregate a few new-born grubs in a glass
tube and give them for their materials some
split pieces of straw, picked from among the
old stalks of a sort of dandelion, *Pterotheca*

nemausensis. Though robbed of the inherit-
ance of the maternal manor, the grubs seem
very well satisfied with my bits. Without the
least hesitation, they scrape out of them a
superb white pith and make it into a delicious
cloak, much handsomer than that which they
would have obtained with the ruins of the
native house, this latter cloak being always
more or less flawed with darker materials,
whose colour has been impaired by long exposure to the air. On the other hand, the
Nîmes dandelion, a relic of last spring, has its
central part, which I myself lay bare, a spotless white; and the cotton nightcap achieves
the very perfection of whiteness.

I obtain an even better result with rounds
of sorghum-pith taken from the kitchen-
broom. This time, the work has glittering
crystalline points and looks like a thing built
of grains of sugar. It is my manufacturers'
masterpiece.

These two successes authorize me to vary
the raw material still further. In the absence
of new-born caterpillars, who are not always
at my disposal, I employ grubs which I have
undressed, that is to say, which I have taken
out of their caps. To these divested ones I

give, as the only thing to work upon, a strip of paper free from paste and easy to pick to pieces, in short, a piece of blotting-paper.

Here again there is no hesitation. The grubs lustily scrape this surface, new to them though it be, and make themselves a paper coat of it. Cadet Roussel,[1] of famous memory, had a coat of similar stuff, but much less fine and silky. My paper-clad charges are so well-pleased with their materials that they scorn their native case, when it is afterwards placed at their disposal, and continue to scrape lint from the industrial product.

Others are given nothing in their tube, but are able to get at the cork that closes the glass dwelling-house. This is enough. The undraped ones hasten to scrape the cork, to break it into atoms and out of these to make themselves a granulated frock, as faultlessly elegant as though their race had always made use of this material. The novelty of the stuff, employed perhaps for the first time, has made no change in the cut of the coat.

[1] A fictitious character, a sort of dolt, created by some wit in a French regiment quartered in Brabant about the year 1792. Cadet Roussel's entertaining exploits were perpetuated in a contemporary ballad.—*Translator's Note.*

The Life of the Caterpillar

To sum up, they accept any vegetable matter that is dry, light and not too resistant. Would they behave likewise towards animal materials and especially mineral materials, on condition that these are of a suitable thinness? I take a Great Peacock's wing, left over from my experiments in the nuptial telegraphy of this Moth,[1] and cut from it a strip on which I place, at the bottom of a tube, two little caterpillars stripped of their clothing. The two prisoners have nothing else at their disposal. Any drapery that they want must be got out of this scaly expanse.

They hesitate for a long time in the presence of that strange carpet. In twenty-four hours' time, one of the caterpillars has started no work and seems resolved to let himself die, naked as he is. The other, stouter-hearted, or perhaps less injured by the brutal stripping-process, explores the slip for a little while and at last resolves to make use of it. Before the day is over, he has clothed himself in grey velvet out of the Great Peacock's scales. Considering the delicacy of the materials, the work is exquisitely correct.

[1] Cf. Chapter XI. of the present volume.—*Translator's Note.*

The Psyches: the Cases

Let us go a step farther in our explorations. For the soft, yielding wadding collected from a plant, or the down gleaned from the wing of a Moth, we will substitute rough stone. In their final state, I know, the Psyches' cases are often laden with grains of sand and earthy particles; but these are accidental bricks, which have been inadvertently touched by the spinneret and incorporated unintentionally in the thatch. The delicate creatures know too well the drawbacks of a pebbly pillow to seek the support of stone. Mineral matter is distasteful to them; and it is mineral matter that now has to be worked like wool.

True, I select such stones in my collection as are least out of keeping with the feeble powers of my grubs. I possess a specimen of flaky hematite. At the merest touch of a hair-pencil it breaks into atoms almost as minute as the dust which a Butterfly's wing leaves on our fingers. On a bed of this material, which glitters like a steel filing, I establish four young caterpillars extracted from their clothing. I foresee a check in this experiment and consequently increase the number of my subjects.

The Life of the Caterpillar

It is as I thought. The day passes and the four caterpillars remain bare. Next day, however, one, one alone, decides to clothe himself. His work is a tiara with metallic facets, in which the light plays with flashes of every colour of the rainbow. It is very rich, very sumptuous, but mightily heavy and cumbrous. Walking becomes laborious under that load of metal. Even so must a Byzantine emperor have progressed at ceremonies of state, after donning his gold-worked dalmatic.

Poor little creature! More sensible than man, you did not select that ridiculous magnificence of your own free will; it was I who forced it on you. Here, to make amends, is a disk of sorghum-pith. Fling off your proud tiara, thrust it from you quickly and place in its stead a cotton night-cap, which is much healthier. This is done on the second day.

The Psyche has his favourite materials when starting as a manufacturer: a vegetable lint collected from any ligneous scrap well softened by the air, a lint usually supplied by the old roof of the maternal hut. In the absence of the regulation fabric, he is able to make use of animal velvet, in particular of the

scaly fluff of a Moth. In case of necessity, he
does not shrink from acts of sheer madness:
he weaves mineral matter, so urgent is his
need to clothe himself.

This need outweighs that of nourishment.
I take a young caterpillar from his grazing-
ground, a leaf of very hairy hawkweed which,
after many attempts, I have found to suit him
as food because of its green blade and as wool
because of its white fleece. I take him, I say,
from his refectory and leave him to fast for
a couple of days. Then I strip him and put
him back on his leaf. And I see him, unmind-
ful of eating, in spite of his long fast, first
labouring to make himself a new coat by collecting the hairs of the hawkweed. His appetite will be satisfied afterwards.

Is he then so susceptible to cold? We are
in the midst of the dog-days. The sun shoots
down a fiery torrent that brings the wild con-
cert of the Cicadæ up to fever-pitch. In the
baking heat of the study where I am questioning my animals, I have flung off hat and necktie and am working in my shirt-sleeves; and,
in this oven, what the Psyche clamours for is,
above all things, a warm covering. Well, little shiverer, I will satisfy you!

The Life of the Caterpillar

I expose him to the direct rays of the sun, on the window-ledge. This time, it is too much of a good thing; I have gone beyond all bounds. The sun-scorched one wriggles about, flourishes his abdomen, always a sign of discomfort. But the making of the hawk-weed cassock is not suspended on this account; on the contrary, it is pursued more hurriedly than ever. Could this be because of the excessive light? Is not the cotton-wool bag a retreat wherein the caterpillar isolates himself, sheltering from the importunities of broad daylight, and gently digests and sleeps? Let us get rid of the light, while retaining a warm temperature.

After a preliminary stripping, the little caterpillars are now lodged in a cardboard box, which I place in the sunniest corner of my window. The temperature here is well over 100° F. No matter: the swan's-down sack is remade at a sitting of a few hours. Tropical heat and the quiet that goes with darkness have made no difference in the insect's habits.

Neither the degree of heat nor the degree of light explains the pressing need of raiment. Where are we to seek the reason for

that hurry to get clad? I can see none save
a presentiment of the future. The Psyche
caterpillar has the winter before him. He
knows nothing of a common shelter in a
silken purse, of cabins among close-touching
leaves, of underground cells, of retreats under
old cracked bark, of hairy roofs, of cocoons,
in short of the different methods employed
by other caterpillars to protect themselves
against the severity of the weather. He has
to spend the winter exposed to the inclemencies of the air. This peril causes his particular talent.

He builds himself a roof whose imbricated
and diverging stalks will allow cold dews and
drops of melted snow to trickle away at a
distance, when the case is fixed and hanging
vertically. Under this covering, he weaves a
thick silk lining, which will make a soft mattress and a rampart against the effects of the
cold. Once these precautions are taken,
the winter may come and the north wind
rage: the Psyche is sleeping peacefully in his
hut.

But all this is not improvised as the stormy
season approaches. It is a delicate work
which takes time to carry out. All his life-

The Life of the Caterpillar

long the caterpillar labours at it, improving
it, adding to it, strengthening it incessantly.
And, in order to acquire greater skill, he begins his apprenticeship at the moment when
he leaves the egg. As preliminary practice
for the thick overcoat of full-grown age, he
tries his hand on cotton capes. Even so does
the Pine Processionary, as soon as hatched,
weave first delicate tents, then gauzy cupolas,
as harbingers of the mighty wallet in which
the community will make its home. Both
alike are harassed from the day of their
birth by the presentiment of the future;
they start life by binding themselves appren-
tices to the trade that is to safeguard them
one day.

No, the Psyche is not more sensitive to
cold than any other smooth-skinned caterpillar; he is a creature of foresight. Deprived in winter of the shelters granted to
the others, he prepares himself, from his
birth, for the building of a home that will
be his salvation and practises for it by making fripperies of wadding suited to his
strength. He foresees the rigours of winter
during the blazing dog-days.

They are now all clad, my young caterpil-

lars, numbering nearly a thousand. They
wander restlessly in large glass receptacles,
closed with a sheet of glass. What do you
seek, little ones, swinging your pretty, snow-
white cloaks as you go? Food, of course.
After all that fatigue, you need refreshment. Despite your numbers, you will not
be too heavy a burden on my resources: you
can manage with so little! But what do you
ask for? You certainly do not count on me
for your supplies. In the open fields you
would have found victuals to your liking
much more easily than I can hope to find them
for you. Since my wish to know all about
you places you in my charge, I have a duty
which I must observe: that of feeding you.
What do you want?

The part of Providence is a very difficult
one to play. The purveyor of foodstuffs,
thinking of the morrow, taking his precautions so that the home may be always more or
less supplied, performs the most deserving but
also the most laborious of functions. The
little ones wait trustingly, persuaded that
things happen of themselves, while he anxiously resorts to every kind of ingenuity and
trouble, wondering whether the right thing

The Life of the Caterpillar

will come. Ah, how well long practice has
taught me to know the trade, with all its wor-
ries and all its joys!

Behold me to-day the Providence of a thousand nurselings thrust upon me by my studies.
I try a little of everything. The tender leaves
of the elm appear to suit. If I serve them up
one day, I find them next morning nibbled on
the surface, in small patches. Tiny grains of
impalpable black dust, scattered here and
there, tell me that the intestines have been
at work. This gives me a moment of satisfaction which will be readily understood by
any breeder of a herd whose diet is unknown.
The hope of success gains strength: I know
how to feed my vermin. Have I discovered
the best method at the first attempt? I dare
not think so.

I continue therefore to vary the fare, but
the results hardly come up to my wishes. The
flock refuses my assorted green stuff and even
ends by taking a dislike to the elm-leaves. I
am beginning to believe that I have failed utterly, when a happy inspiration occurs to me.
I have recognized among the bits that go to
form the case a few fragments of the mouse-
ear hawkweed *(Hieracium pilosella)*. So the

234

The Psyches: the Cases

Psyche frequents that plant. Why should he not browse it? Let us try.

The mouse-ear displays its little round flowers in profusion in a stony field just beside my house, at the foot of the wall where I have so often found Psyche-cases hanging. I gather a handful and distribute it among my different folds. This time the food-problem is solved. The Psyches forthwith settle in solid masses on the hairy leaves and nibble at them greedily in small patches, in which the epidermis of the other surface remains untouched.

We will leave them to their grazing, with which they seem quite satisfied, and ask ourselves a certain question relating to cleanliness. How does the little Psyche get rid of his digestive refuse? Remember that he is enclosed in a sack. One dare not entertain the thought of ordure ejected and accumulating at the far end of the dazzling white plush cap. Filth cannot dwell under so elegant a covering. How is the sordid evacuation managed?

Despite the fact that it ends in a conical point, in which the lens reveals no break of continuity, the sack is not closed at the hind-

The Life of the Caterpillar

er end. Its method of manufacture, by
means of a waistband whose fore-edge increases in dimensions in proportion as the
rear-edge is pushed farther back, proves this
sufficiently. The hinder end becomes pointed
simply owing to the shrinking of the material,
which contracts of itself at the part where the
caterpillar's decreasing diameter no longer
distends it. There is thus at the point a permanent hole whose lips remain closed. The
caterpillar has only to go a little way back
and the stuff expands, the hole widens, the
road is open and the excretions fall to the
ground. On the other hand, so soon as the
caterpillar takes a step forward into his case,
the rubbish-shoot closes of itself. It is a very
simple and very ingenious mechanism, as good
as anything contrived by our seamstresses to
cope with the shortcomings of a boy's first
pair of breeches.

Meanwhile the grub grows and its tunic
continues to fit it, is neither too large nor too
small, but just the right size. How is this
done? If the text-books were to be credited,
I might expect to see the caterpillar split his
sheath lengthwise when it became too tight
and afterwards enlarge it by means of a piece

woven between the edges of the rent. That is what our tailors do; but it is not the Psyches' method at all. They know something much better. They keep on working at their coat, which is old at the back, new in front and always a perfect fit for the growing body.

Nothing is easier than to watch the daily progress in size. A few caterpillars have just made themselves a hood of sorghum-pith. The work is perfectly beautiful; it might have been woven out of snow-flakes. I isolate these smartly-dressed ones and give them as weaving-materials some brown scales chosen from the softest parts that I can find in old bark. Between morning and evening, the hood assumes a new appearance: the tip of the cone is still a spotless white, but all the front part is coarse drapery, very different in colouring from the original plush. Next day, the sorghum felt has wholly disappeared and is replaced, from one end of the cone to the other, by a frieze of bark.

I then take away the brown materials and put sorghum-pith in their stead. This time the coarse, dark stuff retreats gradually towards the top of the hood, while the soft, white stuff gains in width, starting from the

237

mouth. Before the day is over, the original elegant mitre will be reconstructed entirely.

This alternation can be repeated as often as we please. Indeed, by shortening each period of work, we can easily obtain, with the two sorts of material, composite products, showing alternate light and dark belts.

The Psyche, as you see, in no way follows the methods of our tailors, with their piece taken out and another piece let in. In order to have a coat always to his size, he never ceases working at it. The particles collected are constantly being fixed just at the edge of the sack, so that the new drapery increases progressively in dimensions, keeping pace with the caterpillar's growth. At the same time the old stuff recedes, is driven back towards the tip of the cone. Here, through its own springiness, it contracts and closes the muff. Any surplus matter disintegrates, falls into shreds and gradually disappears as the insect roams about and knocks against the things which it meets. The case, new at the front and old at the back, is never too tight because it is always being renewed.

After the very hot period of the year, there comes a moment when light wraps are no

The Psyches: the Cases

longer seasonable. Autumnal rains threaten,
followed by winter frosts. It is time to make
ourselves a thick great-coat with a cape of
thatch arranged in a series of waterproof tip-
pets. It begins with a great lack of accuracy.
Straws of uneven length and bits of dry leaves
are fastened, with no attempt at order, behind
the neck of the sack, which must still retain
its flexibility so as to allow the caterpillar to
bend freely in every direction.

Few as yet, rather short and placed anyhow, sometimes lengthways and sometimes
across, these untidy first logs of the roof will
not interfere with the final regularity of the
building: they are destined to disappear and
will be pushed back and be driven out at last
as the sack grows in front.

Later on, when the pieces are longer and
better-chosen, they are all carefully laid longitudinally. The placing of a straw is done
with surprising quickness and dexterity. If
the log which he has found suits him, the
caterpillar takes it between his legs and turns
it round and round. Gripping it with his
mandibles by one end, as a rule he removes
a few morsels from this part and immediately
fixes them to the neck of the sack. His ob-

ject in laying bare the raw and rough surfaces, to which the silk will stick better, may
be to obtain a firmer hold. Even so the
plumber gives a touch of the file at the point
that is to be soldered.

Then, by sheer strength of jaw, the caterpillar lifts his beam, brandishes it in the air
and, with a quick movement of his rump, lays
it on his back. The spinneret at once sets to
work on the end caught. And the thing is
done: without any groping about or correct-
ing, the log is added to the others, in the direction required.

The fine days of autumn are spent in toil of
this kind, performed leisurely and intermit-
tently, when the stomach is full. By the time
that the cold weather arrives, the house is
ready. When the air is once more warm, the
Psyche resumes his walks abroad: he roams
along the paths, strolls over the friendly
greensward, takes a few mouthfuls and then,
when the hour has come, prepares for his
transformation by hanging from the wall.

These springtime wanderings, long after
the case is completely finished, made me want
to know if the caterpillar would be capable of
repeating his sack-weaving and roof-building

The Psyches: the Cases

operations. I take him out of his case and place him, stark naked, on a bed of fine, dry sand. I give him as materials to work with some old stalks of Nîmes dandelion, cut up into sticks of the same length as the pieces that make the case.

The evicted insect disappears under the heap of ligneous straws and hurriedly starts spinning, taking as pegs for its cords anything that its lips encounter: the bed of sand under-foot, the canopy of twigs overhead. So doing, it binds together, in extricable confusion, all the pieces touched by the spinneret, long and short, light and heavy, at random. In the centre of this tangled scaffolding, a work is pursued of a quite different nature from that of hut-building. The caterpillar weaves and does nothing else, not even attempting to assemble into a proper roofing the materials of which he is able to dispose.

The Psyche owning a perfect case, when he resumes his activity with the fine weather, scorns his old trade as an assembler of logs, a trade practised so zealously during the pre-vious summer. Now that his stomach is satis-fied and his silk-glands distended, he devotes his spare time solely to improving the quilting

of his case. The silky felt of the interior is
never thick or soft enough to please him. The
thicker and softer it is, the better for his own
comfort during the process of transformation
and for the safety of his family afterwards.

Well, my knavish tricks have now robbed
him of everything. Does he perceive the disaster? Though the silk and timber at his
disposal permit, does he dream of rebuilding
the shelter, so essential first to his chilly back
and secondly to his family, who will cut it up
to make their first home? Not a bit of it.
He slips under the mass of twigs where I let
it fall and there begins to work exactly as
he would have done under normal conditions.

This shapeless roof and this sand on which
the jumble of rafters are lying now represent
to the Psyche the walls of the regulation
home; and, without in any way modifying his
labours to meet the exigencies of the moment,
the caterpillar upholsters the surfaces within
his reach with the same zest that he would
have displayed in adding new layers to the
quilted lining which has disappeared. Instead
of being pasted on the proper wall, the present hangings come in contact with the rough
surface of the sand and the hopeless tangle

of the straws; and the spinner takes no notice.

The house is worse than ruined: it no longer exists. No matter: the caterpillar continues his actual work; he loses sight of the real and upholsters the imaginary.[1] And yet everything ought to apprise him of the absence of any roofing. The sack with which he has managed to cover himself, very skilfully for that matter, is lamentably flabby. It sags and rumples at every movement of the insect's body. Moverover, it is made heavy with sand and bristles with spikes in every direction, which catch in the dust of the road and make all progress impossible. Thus anchored to the ground, the caterpillar wastes his strength in efforts to shift his position. It takes him hours to make a start and to move his cumbrous dwelling a fraction of an inch.

With his normal case, in which all the beams are imbricated from front to back with scientific precision, he gets along very nimbly.

[1] For other instances of what Fabre calls "the insect's mental incapacity in the presence of the accidental" I would refer the reader to one essay *inter alia,* entitled, *Some Reflections upon Insect Psychology,* which forms chap. vii. of *The Mason-bees.—Translator's Note.*

The Life of the Caterpillar

His collection of logs, all fixed in front and all free at the back, forms a boat-shaped sledge which slips and glides through obstacles without difficulty. But, though progress be easy, retreat is impracticable, for each piece of the framework causes the thing to stop, owing to its free end.

Well, the sack of my victim is covered with laths pointing this way and that, just in the position in which they happened to be caught by the spinneret, as it fastened its threads here and there, indiscriminately. The bits in front are so many spurs which dig into the sand and neutralize all efforts to advance; the bits at the side are rakes whose resistance cannot be overcome. In such conditions, the insect is bound to be stranded and to perish on the spot.

If I were advising the caterpillar, I should say:

"Go back to the art in which you excel; arrange your bundle neatly; point the cumbrous pieces lengthwise, in an orderly fashion; do something to your sack, which hangs too loosely; give it the necessary stiffness with a few props to act as a busk; do now, in your distress, what you knew so well how to do before; summon up your old carpentering-talents and you will be saved."

Useless advice! The time for carpentry is over. The hour has come for upholstering; and he upholsters obstinately, padding a house which no longer exists. He will perish miserably, cut up by the Ants, as the result of his too-rigid instinct.

Many other instances have already told us as much. Like running water which does not climb slopes and which does not flow back to its source, the insect never retraces its actions. What is done is done and cannot be recommenced. The Psyche, but now a clever carpenter, will die for want of knowing how to fix a beam.

CHAPTER XI

THE GREAT PEACOCK

IT WAS a memorable evening. I shall call it the Great Peacock evening. Who does not know the magnificent Moth, the largest in Europe, clad in maroon velvet with a necktie of white fur? The wings, with their sprinkling of grey and brown, crossed by a faint zig-zag and edged with smoky white, have in the centre a round patch, a great eye with a black pupil and a variegated iris containing successive black, white, chestnut and purple arcs.

No less remarkable is the caterpillar, in colour an undecided yellow. On the top of thinly-scattered tubercles, crowned with a palisade of black hairs, are set beads of turquoise blue. His stout brown cocoon, so curious with its exit-shaft shaped like an eel-trap, is usually fastened to the bark at the base of old almond-trees. The caterpillar feeds on the leaves of the same tree.

Well, on the morning of the 6th of May, a female emerges from her cocoon in my

The Great Peacock

presence, on the table of my insect-laboratory. I forthwith cloister her, still damp with the humours of the hatching, under a wire-gauze bell-jar. For the rest, I cherish no particular plans. I incarcerate her from mere habit, the habit of the observer always on the look-out for what may happen.

It was a lucky thought. At nine o'clock in the evening, just as the household is going to bed, there is a great stir in the room next to mine. Little Paul, half-undressed, is rushing about, jumping and stamping, knocking the chairs over like a mad thing. I hear him call me:

"Come quick!" he screams. "Come and see these Moths, big as birds! The room is full of them!"

I hurry in. There is enough to justify the child's enthusiastic and hyperbolical exclamations, an invasion as yet unprecedented in our house, a raid of giant Moths. Four are already caught and lodged in a bird-cage. Others, more numerous, are fluttering on the ceiling.

At this sight, the prisoner of the morning is recalled to my mind.

"Put on your things, laddie," I say to my

son. "Leave your cage and come with me. We shall see something interesting."

We run downstairs to go to my study, which occupies the right wing of the house. In the kitchen I find the servant, who is also bewildered by what is happening and stands flicking her apron at great Moths whom she took at first for Bats.

The Great Peacock, it would seem, has taken possession of pretty well every part of the house. What will it be around my prisoner, the cause of this incursion? Luckily, one of the two windows of the study had been left open. The approach is not blocked.

We enter the room, candle in hand. What we see is unforgetable. With a soft flick-flack the great Moths fly around the bell-jar, alight, set off again, come back, fly up to the ceiling and down. They rush at the candle, putting it out with a stroke of their wings; they descend on our shoulders, clinging to our clothes, grazing our faces. The scene suggests a wizard's cave, with its whirl of Bats. Little Paul holds my hand tighter than usual, to keep up his courage.

How many of them are there? About a score. Add to these the number that have

The Great Peacock

strayed into the kitchen, the nursery and the other rooms of the house; and the total of those who have arrived from the outside cannot fall far short of forty. As I said, it was a memorable evening, this Great Peacock evening. Coming from every direction and apprised I know not how, here are forty lovers eager to pay their respects to the marriageable bride born that morning amid the mysteries of my study.

For the moment let us disturb the swarm of wooers no further. The flame of the candle is a danger to the visitors, who fling themselves into it madly and singe their wings. We will resume the observation tomorrow with an experimental interrogatory thought out beforehand.

But first let us clear the ground and speak of what happens every night during the week that my observation lasts. Each time it is pitch dark, between eight and ten o'clock, when the Moths arrive one by one. It is stormy weather, the sky is very much overcast and the darkness is so profound that even in the open air, in the garden, far from the shadow of the trees, it is hardly possible to see one's hand before one's face.

The Life of the Caterpillar

In addition to this darkness there is the difficulty of access. The house is hidden by tall plane-trees; it is approached by a walk thickly bordered with lilac- and rose-trees, forming a sort of outer vestibule; it is protected against the mistral by clumps of pines and screens of cypresses. Clusters of bushy shrubs make a rampart a few steps away from the door. It is through this tangle of branches, in complete darkness, that the Great Peacock has to tack about to reach the object of his pilgrimage.

Under such conditions, the Brown Owl would not dare leave the hole in his olive-tree. The Moth, better-endowed with his faceted optical organs than the night-bird with its great eyes, goes forward without hesitating and passes through without knocking against things. He directs his tortuous flight so skilfully that, despite the obstacles overcome, he arrives in a state of perfect freshness, with his big wings intact, with not a scratch upon him. The darkness is light enough for him.

Even if we grant that it perceives certain rays unknown to common retinæ, this extraordinary power of sight cannot be what

warns the Moth from afar and brings him
hurrying to the spot. The distance and the
screens interposed make this quite impossible.

Besides, apart from deceptive refractions,
of which there is no question in this case, the
indications provided by light are so precise
that we go straight to the thing seen. Now
the Moth sometimes blunders, not as to the
general direction which he is to take, but as to
the exact spot where the interesting events
are happening. I have said that the children's nursery, which is at the side of the
house opposite my study, the real goal of my
visitors at the present moment, was occupied
by the Moths before I went there with a light
in my hand. These certainly were ill-
informed. There was the same throng of
hesitating visitors in the kitchen; but here the
light of a lamp, that irresistible lure to nocturnal insects, may have beguiled the eager ones.

Let us consider only the places that were
in the dark. In these there are several stray
Moths. I find them more or less everywhere
around the actual spot aimed at. For instance, when the captive is in my study, the
visitors do not all enter by the open window,
the safe and direct road, only two or three

The Life of the Caterpillar

yards away from the caged prisoner. Several of them come in downstairs, wander about the hall and at most reach the staircase, a blind alley barred at the top by a closed door.

These data tell us that the guests at this nuptial feast do not make straight for their object, as they would if they derived their information from some kind of luminous radiation, whether known or unknown to our physical science. It is something else that apprises them from afar, leads them to the proximity of the exact spot and then leaves the final discovery to the airy uncertainty of random searching. It is very much like the way in which we ourselves are informed by hearing and smell, guides which are far from accurate when we want to decide the precise point of origin of the sound or the smell.

What are the organs of information that direct the rutting Moth on his nightly pilgrimage? One suspects the antennæ, which, in the males, do in fact seem to be questioning space with their spreading tufts of feathers. Are those glorious plumes mere ornaments, or do they at the same time play a part in the perception of the effluvia that guide the enamoured swain? A conclusive experiment seems to present no difficulty. Let us try it.

On the day after the invasion, I find in the study eight of my visitors of the day before. They are perched motionless on the transoms of the second window, which is kept closed. The others, when their dance was over, about ten o'clock in the evening, went out as they came in, that is to say, through the first window, which is left open day and night. Those eight persevering ones are just what I want for my schemes.

With a sharp pair of scissors, without otherwise touching the Moths, I cut off their antennæ, near the base. The patients take hardly any notice of the operation. Not one moves; there is scarcely a flutter of the wings. These are excellent conditions: the wound does not seem at all serious. Undistraught by pain, the Moths bereft of their horns will adapt themselves all the better to my plans. The rest of the day is spent in placid immobility on the cross-bars of the window.

There are still a few arrangements to be made. It is important in particular to shift the scene of operations and not to leave the female before the eyes of the maimed ones

The Life of the Caterpillar

at the moment when they resume their nocturnal flight, else the merit of their quest would disappear. I therefore move the bell-jar with its captives and place it under a porch at the other end of the house, some fifty yards from my study.

When night comes, I go to make a last inspection of my eight victims. Six have flown out through the open window; two remain behind, but these have dropped to the floor and no longer have the strength to turn over if I lay them on their backs. They are exhausted, dying. Pray do not blame my surgical work. This quick decreptitude occurs invariably, even without the intervention of my scissors.

Six, in better condition, have gone off. Will they return to the bait that attracted them yesterday? Though deprived of their antennæ, will they be able to find the cage, now put in another place, at a considerable distance from its original position?

The cage is standing in the dark, almost in the open air. From time to time, I go out with a lantern and a Butterfly-net. Each visitor is captured, examined, catalogued and forthwith let loose in an adjoining room, of which I close the door. This gradual elimination will enable me to tell the exact number, with no risk of counting the same Moth more than once. Moreover, the temporary gaol, which is spacious and bare, will in no way endanger the prisoners, who will find a quiet retreat there and plenty of room. I shall take similar precautions during my subsequent investigations.

At half past ten no more arrive. The sitting is over. In all, twenty-five males have been caught, of whom only one was without antennæ. Therefore, of the six on whom I operated yesterday and who were hale enough to leave my study and go back to the fields, one alone has returned to the bell-jar. It is a poor result, on which I dare not rely when it comes to asserting or denying that the antennæ play a guiding part. We must begin all over again, on a larger scale.

Next morning I pay a visit to the prisoners of the day before. What I see is not encouraging. Many are spread out on the floor, almost lifeless. Several of them give hardly a sign of life when I take them in my fingers. What can I hope from these cripples? Still, let us try. Perhaps they will recover their vigour when the time comes to dance the lovers' round.

The twenty-four new ones undergo amputation of the antennæ. The old, hornless one is left out of count, as dying or close to it. Lastly, the prison-door is left open for the remainder of the day. He who will may leave the room, he who can shall join in the evening festival. In order to put such as go out to the test of searching for the bride, the cage, which they would be sure to notice on the threshold, is once more removed. I shift it to a room in the opposite wing, on the ground-floor. The access to this room is of course left free.

Of the twenty-four deprived of their antennæ, only sixteen go outside. Eight remain, powerless to move. They will soon die where they are. Out of the sixteen who have left, how many are there that return to the cage in the evening? Not one! I sit up to capture just seven, all newcomers, all sporting feathers. This result would seem to show that the amputation of the antennæ is a rather serious matter. Let us not draw conclusions yet: a doubt remains and an important one.

The Great Peacock

"A nice state I'm in!" said Mouflard, the Bull-pup, when his pitiless breeder had docked his ears. "How dare I show my face before the other Dogs?"

Can it be that my Moths entertain Master Mouflard's apprehensions? Once deprived of their fine plumes, dare they no longer appear amidst their rivals and a-wooing go? Is it bashfulness on their part or lack of guidance? Or might it not rather be exhaustion after a wait that exceeds the duration of an ephemeral flame? Experiment shall tell us.

On the fourth evening, I take fourteen Moths, all new ones, and imprison them, as they arrive, in a room where I intend them to pass the night. Next morning, taking advantage of their daytime immobility, I remove a little of the fur from the centre of their corselet. The silky fleece comes off so easily that this slight tonsure does not inconvenience the insects at all; it deprives them of no organ which may be necessary to them later, when the time comes to find the cage. It means nothing to the shorn ones; to me it means the unmistakable sign that the callers have repeated their visit.

The Life of the Caterpillar

This time there are no weaklings incapable
of flight. At night, the fourteen shaven
Moths escape into the open. Of course the
place of the cage is once more changed. In
two hours, I capture twenty Moths, including
two tonsured ones, no more. Of those who
lost their antennæ two days ago, not one puts
in an appearance. Their nuptial time is over
for good and all.

Only two return out of the fourteen
marked with a bald patch. Why do the
twelve others hang back, although supplied
with what we have assumed to be their guides,
their antennary plumes? Why again that
formidable list of defaulters, which we find
nearly always after a night of sequestration?
I perceive but one reply: the Great Peacock
is quickly worn out by the ardours of pairing-
time.

With a view to his wedding, the one and
only object of his life, the Moth is gifted
with a wonderful prerogative. He is able to
discover the object of his desire in spite of
distance, obstacles and darkness. For two or
three evenings, he is allowed a few hours
wherein to indulge his search and his amorous exploits. If he cannot avail himself of

them, all is over: the most exact of compasses fails, the brightest of lamps expires. What is the use of living after that? Stoically we withdraw into a corner and sleep our last sleep, which is the end of our illusions and of our woes alike.

The Great Peacock becomes a Moth only in order to perpetuate his species. He knows nothing of eating. While so many others, jolly companions one and all, flit from flower to flower, unrolling the spiral of their proboscis and dipping it into the honeyed cups, he, the incomparable faster, wholly freed from the bondage of the belly, has no thought of refreshment. His mouth-parts are mere rudiments, vain simulacra, not real organs capable of performing their functions. Not a sup enters his stomach: a glorious privilege, save that it involves a brief existence. The lamp needs its drop of oil, if it is not to be extinguished. The Great Peacock renounces that drop, but at the same time he renounces long life. Two or three evenings, just time enough to allow the couple to meet, and that is all: the big Moth has lived.

Then what is the meaning of the staying away of those who have lost their antennæ?

The Life of the Caterpillar

Does it show that the absence of these organs has made them incapable of finding the wire bell in which the prisoner awaits them? Not at all. Like the shorn ones, whose operation has left them uninjured, they prove only that their time is up. Whether maimed or intact, they are unfit for duty because of their age; and their non-return is valueless as evidence. For lack of the time necessary for experimenting, the part played by the antennæ escapes us. Doubtful it was and doubtful it remains.

My caged prisoner lives for eight days. Every evening she draws for my benefit a swarm of visitors, in varying numbers, now to one part of the house, now to another, as I please. I catch them, as they come, with the net and transfer them, the moment they are captured, to a closed room, in which they spend the night. Next morning, I mark them with a tonsure on the thorax.

The aggregate of the visitors during those eight evenings amounts to a hundred and fifty, an astounding number when I consider how hard I had to seek during the following two years to collect the materials necessary for continuing these observations. Though

The Great Peacock

not impossible to find in my near neighbourhood, the cocoons of the Great Peacock are
at least very rare, for old almond-trees, on
which the caterpillars live, are scarce in these
parts. For two winters I visited every one of
those decayed trees at the lower part of the
trunk, under the tangle of hard grasses in
which they are clad, and time after time I
returned empty-handed. Therefore my hundred and fifty Moths came from afar,
from very far, within a radius of perhaps a mile and a half or more. How
did they know of what was happening in my
study?

The perceptive faculties can receive information from a distance by means of three
agents: light, sound and smell. Is it permis-
sible to speak of vision in this instance? I
will readily admit that sight guides the visitors once they have passed through the open
window. But before that, in the mystery out
of doors! It would not be enough to grant
them the fabulous eye of the Lynx, which was
supposed to see through walls; we should
have to admit a keenness of sight which could
be exercised miles away. It is useless to discuss anything so outrageous; let us pass on.

The Life of the Caterpillar

Sound is likewise out of the question. The great fat Moth, capable of sending a summons to such a distance, is mute even to the most acute hearing. It is just possible that she possesses delicate vibrations, passionate quivers, which might perhaps be perceptible with the aid of an extremely sensitive microphone; but remember that the visitors have to be informed at considerable distances, thousands of yards away. Under these conditions, we cannot waste time thinking of acoustics. That would be to set silence the task of waking the surrounding air.

There remains the sense of smell. In the domain of our senses, scent, better than anything else, would more or less explain the onrush of the Moths, even though they do not find the bait that allures them until after a certain amount of hesitation. Are there, in point of fact, effluvia similar to what we call odour, effluvia of extreme subtlety, absolutely imperceptible to ourselves and yet capable of impressing a sense of smell better-endowed than ours? There is a very simple experiment to be made. It is a question of masking those effluvia, of stifling them under a powerful and persistent odour, which masters the olfactory sense entirely. The too-strong scent will neutralize the very faint one.

I begin by sprinkling naphthaline in the room where the males will be received this evening. Also, in the bell-jar, beside the female, I lay a big capsule full of the same stuff. When the visiting-hour comes, I have only to stand in the doorway of the room to get a distinct smell of gas-works. My artifice fails. The Moths arrive as usual, they enter the room, pass through its tarry atmosphere and make for the cage with as much certainty of direction as though in unscented surroundings.

My confidence in the olfactory explanation is shaken. Besides, I am now unable to go on. Worn out by her sterile wait, my prisoner dies on the ninth day, after laying her unfertilized eggs on the wirework of the cage. In the absence of a subject of experiment, there is no more to be done until next year.

This time I shall take my precautions, I shall lay in a stock so as to be able to repeat as often as I wish the experiments which I have already tried and those which I am contemplating. To work, then; and that without delay.

The Life of the Caterpillar

In the summer, I proclaim myself a buyer of caterpillars at a sou apiece. The offer appeals to some urchins in the neighbourhood, my usual purveyors. On Thursdays, emancipated from the horrors of parsing,[1] they scour the fields, find the fat caterpillar from time to time and bring him to me clinging to the end of a stick. They dare not touch him, poor mites; they are staggered at my audacity when I take him in my fingers as they might take the familiar Silk-worm.

Reared on almond-tree branches, my menagerie in a few days supplies me with magnificent cocoons. In the winter, assiduous searches at the foot of the fostering tree complete my collection. Friends interested in my enquiries come to my assistance. In short, by dint of trouble, much running about, commercial bargains and not a few scratches from brambles, I am the possessor of an assortment of cocoons, of which twelve, bulkier and heavier than the others, tell me that they belong to females.

A disappointment awaits me, for May arrives, a fickle month which brings to naught

[1] Thursday is the weekly holiday in French schools.— *Translator's Note.*

my preparations, the cause of so much anxiety. We have winter back again. The mistral howls, tears the budding leaves from the plane-trees and strews the ground with them. It is as cold as in December. We have to light the fires again at night and resume the thick clothes which we were beginning to leave off.

My Moths are sorely tried. They hatch late and are torpid. Around my wire cages, in which the females wait, one to-day, another to-morrow, according to the order of their birth, few males or none come from the outside. And yet there are some close at hand, for the plumed gallants resulting from my harvest were placed out in the garden as soon as they were hatched and recognized. Whether near neighbours or strangers from afar, very few arrive; and these are only half-hearted. They enter for a moment, then disappear and do not return. The lovers have grown cold.

It is also possible that the low temperature is unfavourable to the tell-tale effluvia, which might well be enhanced by the warmth and decreased by the cold, as happens with scents. My year is lost. Oh, what laborious work is this experimenting at the mercy of the sudden changes and deceptions of a short season!

I begin all over again, for the third time. I rear caterpillars, I scour the country in search of cocoons. When May returns, I am suitably provided. The weather is fine and responds to my hopes. I once more see the incursions which had struck me so powerfully at the beginning, at the time of the historic invasion which first led to my researches.

Nightly the visitors turn up, in squads of twelve, twenty or more. The female, a lusty, big-bellied matron, clings firmly to the trellis-work of the cage. She makes no movement, gives not so much as a flutter of the wings, seems indifferent to what is going on. Nor is there any odour, so far as the most sensitive nostrils in the household can judge, nor any rustle perceptible to the most delicate hearing among my family, all of whom are called in to bear evidence. In motionless contemplation she waits.

The others, in twos or threes or more, flop down upon the dome of the cage, run about it briskly in every direction, lash it with the tips of their wings in continual movement. There are no affrays between rivals. With

not a sign of jealousy in regard to the other
suitors, each does his utmost to enter the enclosure. Tiring of their vain attempts, they
fly away and join the whirling throng of
dancers. Some, giving up all hope, escape
through the open window; fresh arrivals take
their places; and, on the top of the cage, until ten o'clock in the evening, attempts to approach are incessantly renewed, soon to be
abandoned and as soon resumed.

Every evening the cage is moved to a different place. I put it on the north side and
the south, on the ground-floor and the first
floor, in the right wing and fifty yards away
in the left, in the open air or hidden in a distant room. All these sudden displacements,
contrived if possible to put the seekers off the
scent, do not trouble the Moths in the least.
I waste my time and ingenuity in trying to de-
ceive them.

Recollection of places plays no part here.
Yesterday, for instance, the female was
installed in a certain room. The feathered
males came fluttering thither for a couple of
hours; several even spent the night there.
Next day, at sunset, when I move the cage, all
are out of doors. Ephemeral though they be,

the newest comers are ready to repeat their nocturnal expeditions a second time and a third. Where will they go first, these veterans of a day?

They know all about the meeting-place of yesterday. One is inclined to think that they will go back to it, guided by memory, and that, finding nothing left, they will proceed elsewhither to continue their investigations. But no: contrary to my expectations, they do nothing of the sort. Not one reappears in the place which was so thickly crowded last night; not one pays even a short visit. The room is recognized as deserted, without the preliminary enquiry which recollection would seem to demand. A more positive guide than memory summons them elsewhere.

Until now the female has been left exposed, under the meshes of a wire gauze. The visitors, whose eyes are used to piercing the blackest gloom, can see her by the vague light of what to us is darkness. What will happen if I imprison her under an opaque cover? According to its nature, will not this cover either set free or arrest the tell-tale effluvia?

Physical science is to-day preparing to give us wireless telegraphy, by means of the

The Great Peacock

Hertzian waves. Can the Great Peacock have anticipated our efforts in this direction? In order to set the surrounding air in motion and to inform pretenders miles away, can the newly-hatched bride have at her disposal electric or magnetic waves, which one sort of screen would arrest and another let through? In a word, does she, in her own manner, employ a kind of wireless telegraphy? I see nothing impossible in this: insects are accustomed to invent things quite as wonderful.

I therefore lodge the female in boxes of various characters. Some are made of tin, some of cardboard, some of wood. All are hermetically closed, are even sealed with stout putty. I also use a glass bell-jar standing on the insulating support of a pane of glass.

Well, under these conditions of strict closing, never a male arrives, not one, however favourable the mildness and quiet of the evening. No matter its nature, whether of metal or glass, of wood or cardboard, the closed receptacle forms an insuperable obstacle to the effluvia that betray the captive's whereabouts.

A layer of cotton two fingers thick gives the same result. I place the female in a large jar, tying a sheet of wadding over the mouth by way of a lid. This is enough to keep the neighbourhood in ignorance of the secrets of my laboratory. No male puts in an appearance.

On the other hand, make use of ill-closed, cracked boxes, or even hide them in a drawer, in a cupboard; and, notwithstanding this added mystery, the Moths will arrive in numbers as great as when they come thronging to the trellised cage standing in full view on a table. I have retained a vivid recollection of an evening when the recluse was waiting in a hat-box at the bottom of a closed wall-cupboard. The Moths arrived, went to the door, struck it with their wings, knocked at it to express their wish to enter. Passing wayfarers, coming no one knows whence across the fields, they well knew what was inside there, behind those boards.

We must therefore reject the idea of any means of information similar to that of wireless telegraphy, for the first screen set up, whether a good conductor or a bad, stops the female's signals completely. To give these a free passage and carry them to a distance, one condition is indispensable: the receptacle in which the female is contained must be imperfectly closed, so as to establish a communication between the inner and the outer air. This brings us back to the probability of an odour, though that was contradicted by my experiment with naphthaline.

My stock of cocoons is exhausted and the problem is still obscure. Shall I try again another year, the fourth? I abandon the thought for the following reasons: Moths that mate at night are difficult to observe if I want to watch their intimate actions. The gallant certainly needs no illuminant to attain his ends; but my feeble human powers of vision cannot dispense with one at night. I must have at least a candle, which is often extinguished by the whirling swarm. A lantern saves us from these sudden eclipses; but its dim light, streaked with broad shadows, does not suit a conscientious observer like myself, who wants to see and to see clearly.

Nor is this all. The light of a lamp diverts the Moths from their object, distracts them from their business and, if persistent, gravely compromises the success of the evening. The visitors no sooner enter the room than they make a wild rush for the flame, singe their fluff in it and thenceforth, frightened by the scorching received, cease to be trustworthy witnesses. When they are not burnt, when they are kept at a distance by a glass chimney, they perch as close as they can to the light and there stay, hypnotized.

One evening, the female was in the dining-room, on a table facing the open window. A lighted paraffin-lamp, with a large white-enamel shade, was hanging from the ceiling. Two of the arrivals alighted on the dome of the cage and fussed around the prisoner; seven others, after greeting her as they passed, made for the lamp, circled about it a little and then, fascinated by the radiant glory of the opal cone, perched on it, motionless, under the shade. Already the children's hands were raised to seize them.

"Don't," I said. "Leave them alone. Let us be hospitable and not disturb these pilgrims to the tabernacle of light."

All that evening, not one of the seven budged. Next morning, they were still there. The intoxication of light had made them forget the intoxication of love.

With creatures so madly enamoured of the radiant flame, precise and prolonged experiment becomes unfeasible the moment the ob-

The Great Peacock

server requires an artificial illuminant. I give up the Great Peacock and his nocturnal nuptials. I want a Moth with different habits, equally skilled in keeping conjugal appointments, but performing in the day-time.

Before continuing with a subject that fulfils these conditions, let us drop chronological order for a moment and say a few words about a late-comer who arrived after I had completed my enquiries, I mean the Lesser Peacock *(Attacus pavonia minor,* LIN.*)*. Somebody brought me, I don't know where from, a magnificent cocoon loosely wrapped in an ample white-silk envelope. Out of this covering, with its thick, irregular folds, it was easy to extract a case similar in shape to the Great Peacock's, but a good deal smaller. The fore-end, worked into the fashion of an eel-trap by means of free and converging fibres, which prevent access to the dwelling while permitting egress without a breach of the walls, indicated a kinswoman of the big nocturnal Moth; the silk bore the spinner's mark.

And, in point of fact, towards the end of March, on the morning of Palm Sunday, the cocoon with the eel-trap formation provides me with a female of the Lesser Peacock,

The Life of the Caterpillar

whom I at once seclude under a wire-gauze
bell in my study. I open the window to allow
the event to be made known all over the district; I want the visitors, if any come, to find
free entrance. The captive grips the wires
and does not move for a week.

A gorgeous creature is my prisoner, in her
brown velvet streaked with wavy lines. She
has white fur around her neck; a speck of carmine at the tip of the upper wings; and four
large, eye-shaped spots, in which black, white,
red and yellow-ochre are grouped in concen-
tric crescents. The dress is very like that of
the Great Peacock, but less dark in colouring.
I have seen this Moth, so remarkable for size
and costume, three or four times in my life.
It was only the other day that I first saw the
cocoon. The male I have never seen. I only
know that, according to the books, he is half
the size of the female and of a brighter and
more florid colour, with orange-yellow on the
lower wings.

Will he come, the unknown spark, the
plume-wearer on whom I have never set eyes,
so rare does he appear to be in my part of the
country? In his distant hedges will he receive
news of the bride that awaits him on my study

table? I venture to feel sure of it; and I am right. Here he comes, even sooner than I expected.

On the stroke of noon, as we were sitting down to table, little Paul who is late owing to his eager interest in what is likely to happen, suddenly runs up to us, his cheeks aglow. In his fingers flutters a pretty Moth, a Moth caught that moment hovering in front of my study. Paul shows me his prize; his eyes ask an unspoken question.

"Hullo!" I say. "This is the very pilgrim we were expecting. Let's fold up our napkins and go and see what's happening. We can dine later."

Dinner is forgotten in the presence of the wonders that are taking place. With inconceivable punctuality, the plume-wearers hasten to answer the captive's magic call. They arrive one by one, with a tortuous flight. All of them come from the north. This detail has its significance. As a matter of fact, during the past week we have experienced a fierce return of winter. The north wind has been blowing a gale, killing the imprudent almond-blossoms. It was one of those ferocious storms which, as a rule, usher in the

275

spring in our part of the world. To-
day the temperature has suddenly grown
milder, but the wind is still blowing from the
north.

Now at this first visit all the Moths hurrying to the prisoner enter the enclosure from
the north; they follow the movement of the
air; not one beats against it. If their compass
were a sense of smell similar to our own, if
they were guided by odoriferous particles dissolved in the air, they ought to arrive from
the opposite direction. If they came from the
south, we might believe them to be informed
by effluvia carried by the wind; coming as they
do from the north, through the mistral, that
mighty sweeper of the atmosphere, how can
we suppose them to have perceived, at a great
distance, what we call a smell? This reflux
of scented atoms in a direction contrary to the
aerial current seems to me inadmissible.

For a couple of hours, in radiant sunshine, the visitors come and go outside the
front of the study. Most of them search
for a long while, exploring the wall, flitting along the ground. To see their hesitation, one would think that they were at a loss
to discover the exact place of the bait that at-

The Great Peacock

tracts them. Though they have come from very far without mistake, they seem uncertain of their bearings once they are on the spot. Nevertheless, sooner or later they enter the room and pay their respects to the captive, without much importunity. At two o'clock all is over. Ten Moths have been here.

All through the week, each time at noonday, when the light is at its brightest, Moths arrive, but in decreasing numbers. The total is nearly forty. I see no reason to repeat experiments which could add nothing to what I already know; and I confine myself to stating two facts. In the first place, the Lesser Peacock is a day insect, that is to say, he celebrates his wedding in the brilliant light of the middle of the day. He needs radiant sunshine. The Great Peacock, on the contrary, whom he so closely resembles in his adult form and in the work which he does as a caterpillar, requires the dusk of the early hours of the night. Let him who can explain this strange contrast of habits.

In the second place, a powerful air-current, sweeping the other way any particles capable of instructing the sense of smell, does not prevent the Moths' arriving from a direction opposite to that of the odoriferous flux, as our physics imagine it.

If I am to go on with my observations, I want a day Moth; not the Lesser Peacock, who made his appearance too late, at a time when I had nothing to ask him, but another, no matter whom, provided that he be quick at discovering nuptial feasts. Shall I find this Moth?

CHAPTER XII

THE BANDED MONK

YES, I shall find him; indeed I have him already. A little chap of seven, with a wideawake face that doesn't get washed every day, bare feet and a pair of tattered breeches held up by a bit of string, a boy who comes regularly to supply the house with turnips and tomatoes, arrives one morning carrying his basket of vegetables. After the few sous due to his mother for the greens have been counted one by one into his hand, he produces from his pocket something which he found the day before, beside a hedge, while picking grass for the Rabbits:

"And what about this?" he asks, holding the thing out to me. "What about this? Will you have it?"

"Yes, certainly I'll have it. Try and find me some more, as many as you can, and I'll promise you plenty of rides on the roundabout on Sunday. Meanwhile, my lad, here's a penny for you. Don't make a mistake when you give in your accounts; put it somewhere

where you won't mix it up with the turnip-
money."

Dazzled with delight at the sight of so
much wealth, my little ragamuffin promises to
search with a will, already seeing visions of a
fortune to be his.

When he has gone, I examine the thing.
It is worth while. It is a handsome cocoon,
blunt-shaped, not at all unlike the product of
our Silk-worm nurseries, of a firm consistency
and a tawny colour. The cursory information which I have picked up from books of
reference makes me almost certain that it is
the Bombyx of the Oak, the Oak Eggar. If
this is so, what luck! I shall be able to continue my observations and perhaps complete
what the Great Peacock began to show me.

The Oak Eggar is, in fact, a classic; there
is not an entomological treatise but speaks of
his exploits in the wedding-season. They tell
us how a mother hatches in captivity, inside a
room and even hidden in a box. She is far
away from the country, amid the tumult of a
big town. The event is nevertheless divulged
to those whom it concerns in the woods and
the meadows. Guided by some inconceivable
compass, the males arrive, hastening from the

The Banded Monk

distant fields; they go to the box, tap at it, fly round and round it.

I had read of these marvels; but seeing, seeing with one's own eyes, and at the same time experimenting a little is quite another matter. What does my penny purchase hold in store for me? Will the famous Bombyx emerge from it?

Let us call her by her other name: the Banded Monk. This unusual name of Monk is suggested by the male's dress: a monk's frock of a modest rusty brown. But in this case the stuff is a delicious velvet, with a pale transversal band and a little white, eye-shaped dot on the front wings.

The Banded Monk is not, in my region, a common Moth whom we are likely to catch if the fancy takes us to go out with a net at the proper season. I have never seen it about the village, especially not in my lonely enclosure, during all the twenty years that I have spent here. I am not a fervent hunter, I admit; the collector's dead insect interests me very little; I want it alive, in the full exercise of its faculties. But I make up for the absence of the collector's zeal by an attentive eye for all that enlivens the fields. A Moth so

remarkable in size and costume would certainly not have escaped me had I met him.

The little seeker whom I had caught so
nicely with a promise of the roundabout never
made a second find. For three years I re-
quisitioned friends and neighbours, especially
the youngsters, those sharp-eyed scrapers of
the brushwood; I myself scraped a great deal
under masses of dead leaves, inspected stone-
heaps, examined hollow tree-trunks. My
trouble was in vain: the precious cocoon was
nowhere to be found. Suffice it to say that
the Banded Monk is very scarce in my neighbourhood. The importance of this detail will
be seen when the time comes.

As I suspected, my solitary cocoon did belong to the famous Moth. On the 20th
of August there emerges a female, corpulent
and big-bellied, attired like the male, but in a
lighter frock, more in the nankeen style. I
establish her in a wire-gauze bell-jar in the
middle of my study, on the big laboratory-
table, littered with books, pots, trays, boxes,
test-tubes and other engines of science. I
have described the setting before: it is the
same as in the case of the Great Peacock. The
room is lighted by two windows looking out.

on the garden. One is closed, the other is kept open day and night. The Moth is placed between the two, in the shadow, some four or five yards away.

The rest of the day and the following day pass without anything worth mentioning. Hanging by her claws to the front of the trellework, on the side nearest the light, the prisoner is motionless, inert. There is no waving of the wings, no quivering of the antennæ. Even so did the female Great Peacock behave.

The mother Bombyx matures; her tender flesh hardens. By some process of which our science has not the remotest idea, she elaborates an irresistible bait which will bring callers flocking to her from the four corners of the heavens. What takes place in that fat body, what transformations are performed that shall presently revolutionize everything around? Were they known to us, the Moth's nostrums would add a cubit to our stature.

On the third day the bride is ready. The festivities burst into full swing. I was in the garden, already despairing of success, so long were things delayed, when, at about three o'clock in the afternoon, in very hot weather

and brilliant sunshine, I saw a host of Moths
gyrating in the embrasure of the open
window.

It is the lovers coming to call upon their
sweetheart. Some are just leaving the
room, others going in, others again are
perched upon the wall, resting as though
jaded after a long journey. I see some approaching in the distance, over the walls, over
the curtain of cypress-trees. They are hurrying up from all directions, but becoming more
and more rare. I missed the beginning of the
reception; and the guests are nearly all here.

Let us go upstairs. This time, in broad
daylight, without losing a single detail, I once
more witness the bewildering spectacle into
which the great night Moth initiated me. My
study is filled with a swarm of males, whom I
estimate at a glance to number about sixty, as
far as it is possible to make a count in this
seething mass. After circling a few times
round the cage, several go to the open window, but return again forthwith and resume
their evolutions. The most eager perch on
the cage, hustle and trample on one another,
fighting for the good places. Inside the bar-
rier, the captive waits impassively, with her

great paunch hanging against the wires. She gives not a sign of emotion in the presence of the turbulent throng.

Going in or going out, fussing round the cage or flitting through the room, for more than three hours they keep up their frenzied saraband. But the sun is sinking, the temperature becomes a little cooler. Chilled likewise is the ardour of the Moths. Many go out and do not come in again. Others take up their positions in readiness for the morrow; they settle on the transoms of the closed window, as the Great Peacocks did. The celebration is over for to-day. It will certainly be renewed to-morrow, for it is still without result, because of the wires.

But alas, to my great dismay, it is not renewed; and this through my own fault! Late in the day, some one brings me a Praying Mantis, worthy of attention because of her exceptionally small size. Preoccupied with the events of the afternoon, without thinking what I am doing, I hastily place the carnivorous insect in the cage that holds my Bombyx. Not for a moment do I dream that this cohabitation can turn out ill. The Mantis is such a little, slender thing; the other is so obese! And thus I entertained no apprehensions.

Ah, little did I know the bloodthirsty fury of which the grapnelled insect is capable! Next morning, to my bitter astonishment, I find the tiny Mantis devouring the huge Moth. The head and the front part of the breast have already disappeared. Horrible creature! What a disappointment I owe to you! Farewell to my researches, which I had cherished in my imagination all night long; not for three years shall I be able to resume them, for lack of a subject.

Bad luck must not, however, make us forget the little that we have learnt. At one sitting, some sixty males came. Considering the rarity of the Monk and remembering the years of fruitless searches conducted by my assistants and myself, we stand astounded at this number. With a female for a bait, the undiscoverable has suddenly become a multitude.

Now where did they come from? From every quarter and from very far, beyond a doubt. During my years of exploration of my neighbourhood, I have got to know every

The Banded Monk

bush in it and every heap of stones; and I am in a position to declare that there are no Oak Eggars there. To make the swarm that filled my study, the whole of the surrounding district must have contributed, from this side and from that, within a radius which I dare not determine.

Three years pass; and fortune persistently entreated at last grants me two Monk-cocoons. Towards the middle of August, both of them, within a few days of each other, give me a female. This is a piece of luck which will allow me to vary and renew my tests.

I quickly repeat the experiments which have already procured me a most positive reply from the Great Peacock. The pilgrim of the day is no less clever than the pilgrim of the night. He baffles all my tricks. He hastens infallibly to the prisoner, in her wire-gauze cage, in whatever part of the house the apparatus be installed; he is able to discover her hidden in a cupboard; he guesses her secret presence in a box of any kind, provided that it be not tightly closed. He ceases to come, for lack of information, when the casket is hermetically sealed. Thus far we see merely a repetition of the feats of the Great Peacock.

A well-closed box, the air contained in which does not communicate with the outer atmosphere, leaves the Monk in complete ignorance of the prisoner's whereabouts. Not one arrives, even when the box is exposed for every eye to see in the window. This brings back, more urgently than ever, the idea of odoriferous effluvia, intransmissible through a wall of metal, cardboard, wood or glass, no matter which.

When put to the test, the great night Moth was not baffled by the naphthaline, whose powerful smell ought, to my thinking, to mask ultrasubtle emanations, imperceptible to any human nostrils. I repeat the experiment with the Monk. This time I lavish all the resources in the way of scents and stenches that my store of drugs permits.

I place the saucers, partly inside the wire-gauze cage, the female's prison, and partly all round it, in a continuous circle. Some contain naphthaline, others oil of lavender, others paraffin, others, lastly, alkaline sulphurs smelling of rotten eggs. Short of asphyxiating the prisoner, I can do no more.

288

The Banded Monk

These arrangements are made in the morning, so that the room may be thoroughly saturated when the trysting-hour arrives.

In the afternoon, the study has become an
odious laboratory in which the penetrating
aroma of lavender-oil and the foul stench of
sulphuretted hydrogen predominate. Remember that I smoke in this room and plentifully
at that. Will the concentrated odours of a
gas-works, a smoker's divan, a scent-shop,
an oil-well and a chemical factory succeed in
putting off the Monk?

Not at all. A little before three, the Moths
arrive, as numerous as ever. They go to the
cage, which I have taken pains to cover with
a thick kitchen-cloth, so as to increase the difficulty. Though they see nothing after they
have entered, though they are steeped in a
foreign atmosphere in which any subtle fra-
grance should have been annihilated, they fly
towards the prisoner and try to get at her by
slipping under the folds of the cloth. My
artifices are fruitless.

After this reverse, so definite in its results,
which repeats what my naphthaline experiment with the Great Peacock taught me, I
ought, logically speaking, to give up the

theory that odorous effluvia serve as a guide
to the Moths invited to the nuptial feast.
That I did not do so was due to a casual observation. The unexpected, the fortuitous,
often provides us with one of those surprises
which show us the road to the truth, hitherto
sought in vain.

One afternoon, trying to discover whether
sight plays any part in the search, once that
the Moths have entered the room, I place the
female in a glass bell-jar and give her a little
oak-branch, with withered leaves, as a perch.
The apparatus is put on a table, opposite the
open window. On entering, the Moths cannot fail to see the prisoner, standing as she
does where they are bound to pass. The pan
with its layer of sand, in which the female
spent the previous night and the morning under a wire-gauze cover, is in my way. I put
it, without premeditation, on the floor at the
other end of the room, in a corner which is
only dimly lighted. It is seven yards from
the window.

The result of these preparations upsets all
my ideas. Of the Moths arriving, none stops
at the glass bell, where the female is plainly
visible, in the full light. They pass by with

utter indifference. Not a glance in her direction, not an enquiry. They all fly right to the far end of the room, to the dusky corner where I placed the tray and the cage. They alight on the trellised top and explore it at length, flapping their wings and hustling one another a little. All the afternoon, until sunset, they dance around the deserted dome the same saraband to which the actual presence of the female would give rise. At last they fly away, but not all of them. There are persistent ones who refuse to go, rooted to the spot by some magic attraction.

A strange result indeed: my Moths hasten to where there is nothing, take their stand there and will not be dissuaded by the repeated warnings of their eyes; they pass without stopping for a moment by the bell-glass in which the female cannot fail to be perceived by one or other of those coming and going. Befooled by a lure, they pay no attention to the real thing.

What is it that deceives them? The whole of the night before and all this morning, the female has sojourned under the wire-gauze cover, either hanging to the trelliswork, or resting on the sand in the pan. Whatever

The Life of the Caterpillar

she touched, above all with her fat belly apparently, has become impregnated, as the result of long contact, with certain emanations. There you have her bait, her love-philtre; there you have what revolutionizes the world of Monks. The sand retains it for a time and spreads its effluvia around.

It is smell therefore that guides the Moths, that gives them information at a distance. Dominated by the sense of smell, they take no notice of what their eyes tell them; they pass by the glass prison in which their lady-love is now interned; they go to the wires, to the sand, on which the magic cruets have shed their contents; they race to the wilderness where naught remains of the witch but the scented evidence of her sojourn.

The irresistible philtre takes a certain time to elaborate. I picture it as an exhalation which is gradually given off and saturates everything that touches the fat, motionless creature. When the glass bell stands directly on the table or, better still, on a square of glass, the communication between the interior and the outer air is insufficient; and the males, perceiving nothing by the sense of smell, keep away, however long the experiment be con-

tinued. At the actual moment, I cannot sub-
stantiate this non-transmission through a
screen, for, even if I establish ample communication, if I separate the bell from its support by means of three wedges, the Moths
do not come at first, however many there may
be in the room. But wait for half an hour,
more or less: the alembic of feminine flavours
begins its distilling and the rush of visitors
takes place as usual.

Now that I possess these data, this unexpected light on the subject, I am at liberty to
vary my experiments, all of which lead to the
same conclusion. In the morning, I establish
the female under a wire-gauze cover. Her
perch is a little oak-twig similar to the last.
Here, motionless, as though dead, she remains
for long hours, buried in the tuft of leaves
that is to be impregnated with her emanations.
When visiting-time approaches, I withdraw
the twig, perfectly saturated, and lay it on a
chair, near the open window. On the other
hand, I leave the female under her cover, well
in view on the table, in the middle of the
room.

The Moths arrive, first one, then two and
three, soon five and six. They come in, go

out, come in again, fly up and down, go to and
fro, keeping all the time to the neighbourhood of the chair with its oak-branch. Not
one makes for the big table, a few paces farther into the room, where the female is waiting for them under the trellised dome. They
are hesitating, that is clear; they are seeking.

At last they find. And what do they find?
The very twig which in the morning had
served the pot-bellied matron as a bed. With
wings swiftly fluttering, they alight upon the
branch; they explore it above and below,
probe it, lift it and move it, until at last the
little bit of foliage drops on the floor. The
probing between the leaves continues none the
less. Under the buffeting of the wings and
the clawing of the feet, the stick is now running along the ground, like a scrap of paper
pawed by a kitten.

While the twig is moving away with its
band of explorers, two new arrivals come
upon the scene. On their way, they have to
pass the chair, which for a brief spell bore the
leafy stick. They stop at it and eagerly investigate the very spot which but now was
covered by the branch. And yet, in their case
as in that of the others, the real object of their

desires is close by them, under a wire gauze which I have omitted to veil. No one notices it. On the floor, the Monks continue to hustle the mattress on which the female lay in the morning; on the chair, they still fumble at the spot where this bedding was first placed. The sun goes down; the time comes to depart. Besides, the effluvia of passion are growing fainter, are dispersing. The visitors go away without more ado. Good-bye till to-morrow.

The following tests tell me that any material, no matter what, can take the place of the leafy branch, that chance inspiration of mine. Some time in advance, I place the female on a couch of cloth or flannel, of wadding or paper. I even subject her to the hardship of a camp-bed of wood, glass, marble or metal. All these objects, after a contact of sufficient length, have the same powerful attraction for the males as the mother Monk herself. They retain this property to a varying extent, according to their nature. The best are wadding, flannel, dust, sand, in short, porous objects. Metals, marble and glass, on the contrary, soon lose their efficacy. Lastly, anything on which the female has rested communicates its virtue to other places by simple contact, as witness the Moths crowding to the seat of the cane-bottomed chair after the oak-branch had fallen from it.

Let us use one of the best beds, flannel, for instance, and we shall see a curious thing. I place at the bottom of a long test-tube or of a narrow-necked bottle, just wide enough to allow of the Moth's passage, a piece of flannel on which the mother has been lying all the morning. The callers go into the vessels, flounder about, do not know how to get out again. I have invented a mouse-trap for them by means of which I could do terrific execution. Let us release the poor things, remove the piece of stuff and put it away in an hermetically closed box. The infatuated Moths go back to the test-tube, headlong reenter the trap. They are attracted by the effluvia which the saturated flannel has imparted to the glass.

I am fully convinced. To summon the Moths of the district to the wedding, to apprise them at a distance of her presence and to guide them, the bride emits an extremely subtle scent, imperceptible to our own organs of smell. With the mother Monk held to their nostrils, those around me perceive not the least odour, not even the youngest, whose senses are not yet vitiated.

This quintessence easily impregnates every object on which the female rests for any length of time; and thenceforth the actual object becomes as potent a centre of attraction as the mother herself, until the emanations are dispelled.

Nothing visible betrays the bait. On a piece of paper, a recent resting-place around which the visitors crowd, there is not an appreciable trace, no moisture of any kind; the surface is just as clean as before the impregnation.

The product is slowly elaborated and has to accumulate a little while before manifesting its full strength. When taken from her couch and placed elsewhere, the female loses her attractions for the time and becomes an object of indifference; it is the resting-place, saturated by long contact, that draws the newcomers. But the batteries are recharged and the deserted one recovers her power.

The appearance of the warning effluvium is delayed for a longer or shorter period according to the species. The newly-hatched

The Life of the Caterpillar

Moth has to mature for a time and to put **her** distillery in order. A female Great Peacock, born in the morning, sometimes has visitors that same evening, but oftener on the second day, after preparations lasting some forty hours. The female Banded Monk adjourns her summons longer than that: her banns of marriage are not published until after two or three days' waiting.

Let us return for a moment to the problematical functions of the antennæ. The male Monk sports a sumptuous pair, similar to those of the Great Peacock, who vies with him in his matrimonial expeditions. Are we to look upon these hairy feelers as a guiding compass? I repeat, without laying much stress on the matter, my former amputations. None of the patients comes back. We must be chary of drawing inferences, however. The Great Peacock has shown us that the failure to return is due to more serious reasons than amputation of the horns.

Moreover, a second Monk, the Clover Bombyx, nearly akin to the first and, like him, superbly plumed, sets us an exceedingly perplexing problem. He is fairly plentiful around my place; even in the enclosure I find

The Banded Monk

his cocoon, which might easily be confused with that of the Oak Bombyx. I am deceived at first by the resemblance. Out of six cocoons, from which I expected to obtain Banded Monks, six females of the other species hatch at the end of August. Well, around those six females, born in my house, never a male appears, though there is no doubt that the tufted ones are present in the neighbourhood.

If spreading feathered antennæ are really organs for receiving information at a distance, why are not my richly-horned neighbours informed of what is happening in my study? Why do their fine plumes leave them indifferent to events that would bring the Banded Monk hastening up in crowds? Once more, the organ does not determine the aptitude. This one is gifted and that one is not, despite organic similarity.

CHAPTER XIII

THE SENSE OF SMELL

IN PHYSICS we hear of nothing nowadays but the Röntgen rays, which penetrate dense bodies and photograph the invisible for us. A fine discovery, but how insignificant in face of the surprises which the future reserves for us when, better-informed of the why and wherefore of things, we supplement with art the feebleness of our senses and succeed in rivalling, be it ever so little, the keenness of perception revealed by the brute creation.

How enviable, in many cases, is this animal superiority! It teaches us the poverty of our attainments; it declares the mediocrity of our sensory apparatus; it gives us evidence of impressions foreign to our nature; it proclaims realities so far in excess of our attributes that they astound us.

A wretched caterpillar, the Pine Processionary, splits his back into meteorological air-holes which snuff the coming weather and

The Sense of Smell

foretell the squall; the bird of prey, with its incomparably long sight, sees from high in the clouds the Field-mouse squatting on the ground; the blinded Bats guide their flight without injury to themselves amid Spallanzani's[1] inextricable maze of threads; the Carrier-pigeon, though moved a hundred leagues from home, infallibly regains his cote across immensities which he has never traversed unaided; within the limits of her humbler flight, a Bee, the Chalicodoma,[2] also spans the unknown, accomplishes a long journey and returns to her mass of cells.

The man who has never seen a Dog hunting for truffles does not know one of the finest achievements of the sense of smell. Absorbed in its functions, the animal trots along, with its nose to the wind, at a moderate pace. It stops, questions the ground with its nostrils, scratches for a few seconds, without undue excitement, and looks up at its master:

"Here we are," it seems to say, "here we

[1]The Abbé Lazaro Spallanzani (1729-99), an early experimenter in natural history and author of a number of important works on the circulation of the blood, on digestion, on generation and on microscopic animals. Cf. *The Hunting Wasps:* chap. xix.—*Translator's Note.*

[2]Cf. *The Mason-Bees, passim.—Translator's Note.*

are! On my word of honour as a Dog, there's a truffle here."

And it speaks the truth. The master digs at the point indicated. If the trowel goes astray, the Dog shows the man how to put it right by sniffing at the bottom of the hole. Do not be afraid of the stones and roots in between: despite the depth and intervening obstacles, the tuber will come. A Dog's nose cannot lie.

"Subtlety of smell," you say.

I have no objection, if by that you mean that the animal's nasal passages are the organ of perception; but is the thing perceived always a mere smell, in the ordinary acceptation of the word, an effluvium such as our own senses understand it? I have some reason to doubt this. Let us set the matter forth.

I have had the good fortune on several occasions to accompany a Dog who was a great expert at his trade. Certainly he was nothing to look at, this artist whom I was so anxious to see at work: just a Dog, placid and deliberate in his ways, ugly, unkempt; the sort of Dog that you would never admit to your fireside. Talent and poverty often go hand in hand.

The Sense of Smell

His master, a celebrated *rabassier*[1] in the village, convinced that I had no intention of stealing his secrets and one day setting up in competition, allowed me to join him in his expeditions, a favour which he did not often grant. The worthy man was quite willing to fall in with my views, once he saw that I was not an apprentice but merely an enquirer who made drawings[2] and wrote down lists of underground vegetable things, instead of marketing my bagful of treasure-trove, the glory of the Christmas Turkey.

It was agreed between us that the Dog should act as he pleased and receive a bit of bread as his reward after each discovery, indiscriminately. Every spot scratched up by his paws was to be dug and the object indicated extracted without our troubling about its commercial value. In no case was the master's experience to intervene and divert the dog from a spot where practice told him

[1] *Rabasso* is the Provençal for truffle. Hence the word *rabassier* to denote a truffle-hunter.—*Author's Note.*

[2] For some account of Fabre's drawings of the fungi of his district, cf. *The Life of the Fly,* by J. Henri Fabre, translated by Alexander Teixeira de Mattos: chap. xvii.—*Translator's Note.*

that nothing saleable was to be found, for, in drawing up my botanical lists, I preferred wretched and unmarketable products to the choicest morsels, though these of course were welcomed when they appeared.

Thus conducted, the underground botanizing was very fruitful. With his perspicacious nose, the Dog made me gather indifferently the large and the small, the fresh and the putrid, the scented and the unscented, the fragrant and the stinking. I was amazed at my collection, which comprised the greater part of the hypogean fungi in my neighbourhood.

What a variety of structure and above all of odour, the primary quality in this question of scent! There are some that have nothing more noticeable than a vague fungous mustiness, which is more or less evident in all. Some smell of turnips, of rotten cabbage; some are fetid enough to fill the collector's house with their stench. The real truffle alone possesses the aroma dear to the epicure.

If smell, as we understand it, is the Dog's only guide, how does he manage to find his way through all these incongruous odours?

The Sense of Smell

Is he apprised of the contents of the soil by a general emanation, the fungous effluvium common to the different species? In that case an extremely embarrassing question arises.

I paid some attention to the ordinary mushrooms, many of which, as yet invisible, announced their coming as imminent by cracking the surface of the ground. Now I never saw the Dog stop at any of those points where my eyes divined the cryptogam pushing back the earth with the thrust of its cap, points where the ordinary fungous smell was certainly most pronounced. He passed them by scornfully, with not a sniff, with not a stroke of his paw. And yet the thing was underground; and its reek was similar to others which he sometimes pointed out to us.

I came back from the Dog's school with the conviction that the truffle-detecting nose has a better guide than smell, in the sense in which our olfactory powers realize it. It must perceive, in addition, effluvia of a different order, full of mystery to us, who are not equipped accordingly. Light has its dark rays, which are without effect upon our retinæ, but not apparently upon all. Why should not

the domain of smell have its secret emanations, unknown to our senses but perceptible
to a differently constructed organ of smell?

If the scent of the Dog leaves us perplexed
to this extent, that it is impossible for us to
say exactly or even to suspect what it perceives, it at least tells us plainly that we
should be greatly mistaken to compare everything by human standards. The world of
sensations is far larger than the limits of our
sensibility admit. What a number of facts
in the working of the forces of nature escape
us for want of organs delicate enough to perceive them!

The unknown, that inexhaustible field
which the future will cultivate, holds harvests
in store for us beside which our present
knowledge is but a pitiful gleaning. Under
the sickle of science sheaves will one day fall
whose grain to-day would seem a senseless
paradox. Scientific illusions? Not so, if you
please, but undeniable and positive realities,
affirmed by the animal world, which in certain respects has a great advantage over the
world of man.

In spite of his long professional practice,
in spite of the aroma of the tuber which he

The Sense of Smell

is seeking, the *rabassier* cannot guess the
presence of the truffle, which ripens in winter
underground, at a depth of eighteen inches or
so; he needs the aid of the Dog or the Pig,
whose scent pries into the secrets of the soil.
Well, these secrets are known to different insects even better than to our two helpers. In
order to discover the tuber on which their
family of grubs is to be fed, they possess a
scent of exceptional perfection.

Long ago, from truffles dug up spoilt and
teeming with vermin and placed in this condition in a glass jar with a layer of fresh sand,
I obtained first a small red Beetle (*Anisotoma
cinnamomea,* PANZ.) and then various Diptera, including a Sapromyzon, who, with her
sluggish flight and feeble frame, reminds me
of a Fly, clad in yellow velvet, known as
Scatophaga scybalaria, that placid frequenter
of human excrement in autumn.

The latter finds her truffle on the surface
of the ground, at the foot of a wall or hedge,
man's usual hasty refuge in the country; but
how does the other know at what point underground lies hers, or rather her grubs'
truffle? To go down and hunt about in the
depths is beyond her power. Her frail

limbs, which the moving of a grain of sand would warp; her wings, which, if extended, would block her way through a gorge; her dress of stiff silk, militating against a smooth passage: these are all against her. The Sapromyzon is obliged to lay her eggs on the surface of the soil, but she must do so at the very spot beneath which the truffle lies, for the tiny grubs would die if they had to roam at random until they came upon their provender, which is always sparsely distributed.

The truffle-hunting Fly is therefore informed by her sense of smell of the spots favourable to her maternal plans; she possesses the scent of the *rabassier* Dog, indeed probably a better one, for she knows things by nature, having never been taught, whereas her rival has only received an artificial education.

It would be interesting to follow the Sapromyzon's manœuvres, but the idea strikes me as impracticable. The insect is rare, flies away quickly and is soon out of sight. To observe it closely, to watch it at work would involve a great loss of time and a degree of assiduity of which I do not feel capable. Another discoverer of underground fungi shall reveal what the Fly could hardly be expected to show us.

This is a pretty little black Beetle, with a pale and velvety belly, round as a cherry-stone and much the same size. The insect's official title is *Bolboceras gallicus,* MULS. By rubbing the tip of its abdomen against the edge of its wing-cases it emits a soft chirrup similar to that of the little birds when their mother comes home with their food. The male wears a graceful horn on his head, copied on a smaller scale from that of the Spanish Copris.[1]

Deceived by this armour, I at first took the insect for a member of the Dung-beetles' corporation and brought it up as such in captivity. I served it with these stercoral dainties which are most appreciated by its presumed colleagues. But never, no, never did it consent to touch them. Fie, for shame! Dung to a Bolboceras! Well! What on earth did I take him for? The epicure expects something very different. He wants not exactly the truffle of our banquets, but its equivalent.

[1] One of the Dung-beetles. Cf. *The Life and Love of the Insect:* chap. v.—*Translator's Note.*

The Life of the Caterpillar

This characteristic was not displayed to me without patient investigation on my part. At the southern foot of the Sérignan hills, not far from the village, stands a thicket of maritime pines, alternating with rows of cypress-trees. Here, at the season of All Saints, after the autumnal rains, the mushrooms abound that frequent the Coniferæ, in particular the delicious milk-mushroom, which turns green at any part that is bruised and sheds tears of blood when you break it.[1] In the mild days of autumn this is the favourite walk of my household, being far enough to exercise young legs and near enough not to tire them.

They find everything there: old Magpies' nests, formed of bundles of twigs; Jays squabbling with one another, after filling their crops with acorns on the oaks hard by; Rabbits suddenly starting out of a rosemary-bush, showing their little white upturned scuts; Geotrupes[2] hoarding away food for the winter and heaping up their rubbish on the

[1] Cf. *The Life of the Fly:* chap. xviii.—*Translator's Note.*

[2] Cf. *The Life and Love of the Insect:* chap. ix.—*Translator's Note.*

threshold of the burrow. And then lovely sand, soft to the touch, easy to dig into tunnels, easy to build into rows of huts which we thatch with moss and surmount with a bit of reed by way of a chimney; and the delicious lunch off an apple to the sound of the Æolian harps softly sighing through the pine-needles!

Yes, for the children it is a real paradise, where one goes as a reward for well-learnt lessons. The grown-ups also have their share of enjoyment. As far as I am concerned, I have for many years been watching two insects here, without succeeding in discovering their family secrets. One of them is *Minotaurus typhœus*,[1] whose male carries on his corselet three spikes pointing in front of him. The old writers used to call him the Phalangist, because of his armour, which may be compared with the three lines of spears of the Macedonian phalanx.

He is a robust fellow, who cares nothing for the winter. All through the cold season, whenever the weather turns a trifle milder, he leaves his house discreetly, at nightfall, and gathers, in the immediate neighbourhood

[1] A Dung-beetle. Cf. *The Life and Love of the Insect:* chap. x.—*Translator's Note.*

of his burrow, a few Sheep-droppings, ancient, olive-shaped remains dried by the summer sun. He heaps them in a stack at the bottom of his larder, shuts the door and eats. When the provisions are all crumbed and drained of their niggardly juices, he climbs back to the surface and renews his stores. Thus does he spend the winter, never resting from his work, except when the weather is too severe.

The second object of my observations in the pine-wood is the Bolboceras. His burrows, distributed here and there, among those of the Minotaur, are easily distinguished. The Phalangist's are surmounted by a bulky mound the materials of which are heaped into a cylinder as long as one's finger. Each of these rolls is a load of rubbish pushed outside by the digger, thrusting with his back from below. The orifice moreover is closed whenever the Beetle is at home, either enlarging the shaft or peacefully enjoying his possessions.

The Bolboceras' lodging is open and surrounded merely by a padding of sand. Its depth is slight, nine inches, hardly more. It goes straight down in very loose soil. It is easily inspected, therefore, if we take care first to dig a trench in front of it, which will enable us later to cut away the perpendicular wall, slice by slice, with the blade of a knife. The burrow then appears at full length, from top to bottom, in a semicylindrical shape.

Often the violated dwelling-house is empty. The insect has left during the night, having finished its business there and gone to settle elsewhere. The Bolboceras is a nomad, a night-walker, who leaves his home without regret and easily acquires a new one. Sometimes also the insect is found at the bottom of the pit: at one time a male, at another a female, but never the two at a time. The sexes, both equally zealous in digging burrows, work separately, not together. This is not, in fact, a family residence, containing the nursery of the young; it is a temporary abode, dug by each occupant for his own comfort.

Sometimes we find nothing there but the well-sinker, surprised during his work of excavation; sometimes, lastly—and the case is not uncommon—the hermit of the crypt embraces with his legs a small hypogean fungus, either intact or partly consumed. He clutches it convulsively, refuses to be parted from it. It is his booty, his fortune, his

worldly goods. Scattered crumbs tell us that
we have caught him feasting.

Let us take his prize away from him. We
shall see a sort of irregular, rugged purse,
closed on every side and varying in size between a pea and a cherry. Outside it is reddish, rough with little warts; inside it is
smooth and white. The spores, which are
ovoid and diaphanous, are contained, in rows
of eight, in long satchels. By these characteristics we recognize an underground cryp-
togamous product, nearly related to the truffles and known to botanists as *Hydnocystis
arenaria,* TUL.

This throws a light upon the habits of the
Bolboceras and upon the reason why his burrows are so frequently renewed. In the calm
of the twilight, the little gadabout takes to
the fields, chirruping softly as he goes, cheer-
ing himself with song. He explores the soil,
questions it as to its contents, just as the Dog
does when hunting for truffles. His sense of
smell warns him when the coveted morsel is
underneath, covered by a few inches of sand.
Certain of the exact spot where the thing lies,
he digs straight down and never fails to
reach it. As long as the provisions last, he

The Sense of Smell

does not go out again. Blissfully he feeds at
the bottom of the well, heedless of the door
left open or hardly barred.

When no more food remains, he moves,
looking for another loaf, which will become
the excuse for a fresh burrow, to be abandoned in its turn. Each fungus consumed
represents a new house, which is a mere refectory, a traveller's refreshment-room. Thus
are the autumn and spring, the seasons of the
hydnocystis, spent in the pleasures of the
table, from one home to the next.

To study the *rabassier* insect more closely,
in my own house, I should need a little store
of its favourite fare. It would be waste of
time to seek for it myself, by digging at random: the little cryptogam is not so plentiful
that I can hope to strike it with my trowel
without a guide. The truffle-hunter needs his
Dog; my informer shall be the Bolboceras
himself. Behold me turned into a *rabassier*
of a new kind. I reveal my secret, which can
only raise a smile from my original instructor
in underground botany, if he should ever hear
of my singular form of competition.

The subterranean fungi occur only at certain points, often in groups. Now the Beetle

has been this way; with his delicate scent he has recognized the site as good, for the burrows are numerous hereabouts. We will therefore dig near the holes. The clue is accurate. In a few hours, thanks to the tracks left by the Bolboceras, I possess a handful of hydnocystes. It is the first time that I have gathered this particular fungus. Let us now catch the insect. That presents no difficulties: we have only to dig up the burrows.

I make my experiments the same evening, filling a large earthen pan with fresh, sifted sand. With a stick as thick as my finger, I make six vertical tunnels in the sand, two decimetres[1] deep and placed at a suitable distance apart. A hydnocystis is lowered to the bottom of each; and I insert a fine straw, to show me the exact position later. Lastly, I fill up the six cavities with caked sand. When this surface has been carefully smoothed, so that the level is everywhere the same, except for the six straws, landmarks that mean nothing to the Bolboceras, I let loose my captives, covering them with a wire-gauze cage. There are eight of them.

At first there is nothing to see save the in-

[1] 7.8 inches.—*Translator's Note.*

evitable uneasiness due to the incidents of their exhumation, transport and confinement in an unknown place. My exiles from home try to escape, climb up the wire, burrow right at the edge of the enclosure. Night falls and things grow calmer. Two hours later, I come to take a last look at them. Three are still buried under a thin layer of sand. The five others have each dug a perpendicular shaft at the very foot of the straws which tell me where the fungi lie. Next morning, the sixth straw has its well like the others.

This is the moment to see what is happening underground. I remove the sand methodically in vertical slices. At the bottom of each burrow is a Bolboceras eating his truffle, the hydnocystis.

Let us repeat the experiment with the partly-consumed victuals. The result is the same. At one brief, nocturnal spell of work, the dainty is discovered underground and reached by means of a gallery which runs plumb to the spot where the morsel lies. There is no hesitation, no trial excavation guided by guesswork. This is proved by the surface of the soil, which everywhere is just as I left it when I smoothed it down. The

The Life of the Caterpillar

insect could not have made straighter for the
coveted object had it been guided by sight;
it always digs at the foot of the straws, my
sign-posts. The Dog, nosing the ground for
truffles, hardly achieves this degree of precision.

Has the hydnocystis then a very pungent
smell, able to give such positive information
to its consumer's scent? Not at all. To our
nostrils it is a neutral object, devoid of any
appreciable olfactory character. A tiny peb-
ble taken out of the ground would impress us
just as much with its faint aroma of fresh
earth. As a revealer of underground fungous
products, the Bolboceras here rivals the Dog.
He would even rise superior to the Dog, were
he able to generalize. But he is a rigorous
specialist: he knows only the hydnocystis. Nothing else, so far as I am aware, tempts him
to dig.[1]

Both of them search the subsoil very
closely, at the level of the ground; and the
object which they seek is not far down. Were
they farther away, neither the Dog nor the in-

[1] Since writing the above lines, I have found him
eating one of the true Tuberaceæ, *Tuber Requienii,* TUL.,
the size of a cherry.—*Author's Note.*

The Sense of Smell

sect would notice effluvia so subtle, not even the smell of a truffle. To make an impression at a great distance, powerful odours are needed, capable of perception by our olfactory sense. Then the exploiters of the odorous thing come hastening up on all sides from afar.

When, for the purpose of my studies, I require insects that dissect corpses, I expose a dead Mole in the sun, in a distant corner of the enclosure. As soon as the animal swells, distended by the gases of putrefaction, and the skin begins to turn green and the fur to fall from it, up come numbers of Silphæ[1] and Dermestes,[2] Necrophori[3] and other Burying-beetles, of whom one would find not a single specimen in the garden, or even in the neighbourhood, without this bait.

They have been informed by their sense of smell, at a great distance all around, whereas I myself can avoid the stench by taking a few steps back. Compared with their scent, mine is contemptible; but still, in their

[1]Carrion-beetles proper.—*Translator's Note.*
[2]Bacon-beetles.—*Translator's Note.*
[3]Burying-beetles proper.—*Translator's Note.*

case as well as mine, there is really here what our language calls a smell.

I can do better still with the flower of the dragon arum (*Arum dracunculus*), so remarkable for its shape and for its unequalled stench. Imagine a wide, lanceolate blade, of a clarety purple, half a yard long and rolled below into an ovoid pouch the size of a hen's egg. Through the opening of this wallet rises a central column springing from the bottom, a long, bright-green club, encircled at its base by two bracelets, one of ovaries, the other of stamens. Such, briefly described, is the flower, or rather the inflorescence, of the dragon arum.

For two days it exhales a frightful stench of carrion, worse than the proximity of a dead Dog would yield. During the hottest part of the day, with a wind blowing, it is loathsome, unbearable. Let us brave the infected atmosphere and go up to it; we shall behold a curious sight.

Informed by the foul odour, which spreads far and wide, various insects come flying along, such insects as make sausage-meat of small corpses—Toads, Adders, Lizards, Hedgehogs, Moles, Field-mice—which the

The Sense of Smell

husbandman hits with his spade and flings away disembowelled on the foot-path. They swoop down upon the great leaf, which, with its livid purple, looks like a strip of meat gone bad; they caper about, intoxicated by the smell of corpse which they love; they roll down the slope and are swallowed up in the purse. After a few hours of bright sunshine, the receptacle is full.

Let us look inside, through the narrow opening. No elsewhere could you see such a crowd. It is a mad whirl of backs and bellies, of wing-cases and legs, swarming, rolling over and over, amid the snap of interlocked joints, rising and falling, floating and sinking, seething and bubbling without end. It is a drunken revel, an epidemic of delirium tremens.

Some, few as yet, emerging from the mass, climb to the opening by means of the central pole or the walls of the enclosure. Will they take wing and make their escape? Not they! Standing on the brink of the chasm, almost free, they drop back into the whirlpool, in a fresh bout of intoxication. The bait is irresistible. Not one of

them will quit the assembly until the evening,
or perhaps next morning, when the heady
fumes have evaporated. Then the mass becomes disentangled; and the insects extricate
themselves from one another's embraces and
slowly, as it were regretfully, leave the place
and fly away. At the bottom of this devil's
purse remains a heap of dead and dying, of
severed limbs and disjointed wing-cases, the
inevitable result of the frenzied orgy. Soon,
Wood-lice, Earwigs and Ants will arrive and
devour the deceased.

What were they doing there? Were they
the prisoners of the flower? Had it converted itself into a trap which allowed them
to enter, but prevented them from escaping,
by means of a fence of converging hairs?
No, they were not prisoners; they had full
liberty to go away, as is shown by the final
exodus, which is effected without impedi-
ment. Deceived by a false odour, were they
doing their best to instal their eggs, as they
would have done under a corpse? Not that
either. There is no trace of an attempt at
egg-laying in the dragon's purse. They came,
enticed by the smell of a dead body, their supreme delight; they were drunk with corpse;

322

and they spun round frantically in an undertakers' carnival.

When the bacchanal dance is at its height, I try to count the number of the arrivals. I rip up the floral pouch and pour its contents into a flask. Absolutely tipsy though they be, many would escape during the census, which I wish to take accurately. A few drops of carbon bisulphide deprive the crowd of motion. The counting then shows that there were over four hundred. Such was the living billow which I saw surging just now in the dragon's purse.

The throng consists entirely of two families, Dermestes and Saprini,[1] both of whom are very busy in spring turning derelict corpses to account. Here is a complete list of the visitors to a single flower, with the number of representatives of each species: *Dermestes Frischii*, KUGEL., 120; *D. undulatus*, BRAHM, 90; *D. pardalis*, SCHOENH., 1; *Saprinus subnitidus*, DE MARS., 160; *S. maculatus*, ROSS., 4; *S. detersus*, ILLIG., 15; *S. semipunctatus*, DE MARS., 12; *S. æneus*, FABR., 2; *S. speculifer*, LATR., 2. Total: 406.

[1] A species of small carnivorous Beetles.—*Translator's Note.*

The Life of the Caterpillar

Another detail deserves attention just as much as this enormous figure; and that is the complete absence of a number of other genera which are as passionately fond of small corpses as are the Dermestes and Saprini. My charnel-houses of Moles never fail to be visited by the Silphæ and Necrophori: *Silpha sinuata,* FABR.; *S. rugosa,* LIN.; *S. obscura,* LIN.; *Necrophorus vestigator,* HERSCH. The reek of the dragon arum leaves them all indifferent. None of them is represented in the ten flowers which I examine.

Nor are any Diptera, those other devotees of corruption. Several Flies, some grey or bluey, others a metallic green, come up, it is true, settle on the edge of the flower and even find their way into the fetid wallet; but they are almost immediately undeceived and fly away. Only the Dermestes and Saprini stay behind. Why?

My friend Bull, as decent a Dog as ever lived, had this among many other eccentricities: if he found in the dust of the road the dried up corpse of a Mole flattened under the heels of the passers-by, mummified by the heat of the sun, he would revel in rolling himself over it from the tip of his nose to the end

of his tail; he would rub himself in it over
and over again, shaken with nervous spasms,
turning first on one side, then on the other.
It was his sachet of musk, his flask of eau-de-
Cologne. When scented to his liking, he
would get up, shake himself and trot off,
pleased as Punch with his pomade. Let us
not abuse him and, above all, let us not discuss the matter. There are tastes of all kinds
in this world.

Why should not some of the insects that
dote on the smell of the dead have similar
habits? Dermestes and Saprini come to the
dragon arum; all day long they swarm in
throngs, although free to go away; many of
them die in the riot of the orgy. It is no
rich provender that keeps them, for the flower
gives them nothing to eat; it is not a question
of laying eggs, for they take good care not
to settle their grubs in that famine-stricken
spot. What are they doing here, the frenzied
ones? Apparently intoxicating themselves
with fetidness, just as Bull did on the carcass
of a Mole.

And this intoxication of smell attracts them
from every part around, from very far perhaps, one cannot tell. Even so the Necro-

phori, in quest of an establishment for their young, hasten from the fields to my putrefy-ing Moles. Both are informed by a potent smell, which offends our nostrils sixty yards away, but which travels ahead and delights them at distances where our own power of scent ceases.

The hydnocystis, the Bolboceras' treat, has none of these violent emanations, capable of being diffused through space; it is devoid of smell, at least to us. The insect that hunts for it does not come from a distance; it inhabits the very places where the cryptogam lies. However faint the effluvia of the under-ground morsel, the prying epicure, equipped for the purpose, has every facility for per-ceiving them: he operates close by, on the surface of the soil. The Dog's case is the same: he goes along searching, with his nose to the ground. Then, too, the real truffle, the essential object of his quest, possesses a most pronounced odour.

But what are we to say of the Great Pea-cock and the Banded Monk, making their way to the female born in captivity? They hasten from the ends of the horizon. What do they perceive at that distance? Is it really

The Sense of Smell

an odour, as our physiology understands the word? I cannot bring myself to believe it.

The Dog smells the truffle by sniffing the earth, quite close to the tuber; he finds his master at great distances by consulting the scent of his footprints. But is he able to discover the truffle hundreds of yards away, miles away? Can he join his master in the complete absence of a trail? Certainly not. For all his fineness of scent, the Dog is incapable of such a feat, which is performed, however by the Moth, who is put off neither by distance nor by the lack of any traces out of doors of the female hatched on my table.

It is a recognized fact that smell, ordinary smell, the smell that affects our nostrils, consists of molecules emanating from the scented body. The odorous matter dissolves and is diffused throughout the air by communicating to the air its aroma, even as sugar dissolves and is diffused in water by communicating to the water its sweetness. Smell and taste touch each other at some points; in both cases there is a contact between the material particles that give the impression and the sensitive papillæ that receive it.

Nothing can be simpler or clearer than that

the dragon arum elaborates an intensely strong essence with which the air is impregnated and infected all around. Thus the Dermestes and Saprini, those passionate lovers of carrion smells, are informed by molecular diffusion. In the same way, the putrid Toad gives out and disseminates the stinking atoms that are the Necrophorus' delight.

But what is materially emitted by the female Bombyx or Great Peacock? Nothing, according to our sense of smell. And this nothing is supposed, when the males congregate, to saturate an immense circle, several miles in radius, with its molecules! What the horrible stench of the dragon arum is unable to do the absence of odour is believed to accomplish! However divisible matter may be, the mind refuses to accept such conclusions. It would be tantamount to reddening a lake with an atom of carmine, to filling immensity with nothing.

Another argument. When my study is saturated beforehand with pungent odours which ought to overcome and destroy the most delicate effluvia, the male Moths arrive without the least sign of embarrassment.

A loud noise kills the faint note and prevents it from being heard; a bright light eclipses a feeble gleam. These are waves of the same nature. But the roar of thunder cannot cause the least jet of light to pale; nor can the dazzling glory of the sun stifle the least sound. Being of different natures, light and sound do not influence each other.

The experiment with the lavender-oil, naphthaline and the rest would therefore seem to prove that odour proceeds from two sources. For emission substitute undulation; and the problem of the Great Peacock is explained. Without losing any of its substance, a luminous point shakes the ether with its vibrations and fills a circle of indefinite width with light. This must almost express the working of the mother Bombyx' tell-tale discharge. It does not emit molecules: it vibrates; it sets in motion waves capable of spreading to distances incompatible with a real diffusion of matter.

In its entirety, smell would thus seem to have two domains: that of the particles dissolved in the air and that of the ethereal waves. The first alone is known to us. It belongs also to the insect. It is this which informs the Saprinus of the dragon arum's fetidity and the Silpha and Necrophorus of the stench of the Mole.

The second, which is far superior in its range through space, escapes us altogether, because we lack the necessary sensory equipment. The Great Peacock and the Banded Monk know it at the time of the nuptial rejoicings. And many others must share it in various degrees, according to the exigencies of their mode of life.

Like light, odour has its X-rays. Should science one day, instructed by the insect, endow us with a radiograph of smells, this artificial nose will open out to us a world of marvels.

CHAPTER XIV

THE CABBAGE-CATERPILLAR

THE cabbage of our modern kitchen-
gardens is a semi-artificial plant, the produce of our agricultural ingenuity quite as
much as of the niggardly gifts of nature.
Spontaneous vegetation supplied us with the
long-stalked, scanty-leaved, ill-smelling wild-
ing, as found, according to the botanists, on
the ocean cliffs. He had need of a rare inspiration who first showed faith in this rustic
clown and proposed to improve it in his gar-
den-patch.

Progressing by infinitesimal degrees, cul-
ture wrought miracles. It began by persua-
ding the wild cabbage to discard its wretched
leaves, beaten by the sea-winds, and to replace
them by others, ample and fleshy and close-
fitting. The gentle cabbage submitted without protest. It deprived itself of the joys of
light by arranging its leaves in a large, compact head, white and tender. In our day,
among the successors of those first tiny hearts,
are some that, by virtue of their massive bulk,

have earned the glorious name of *chou quintal,* as who should say, a hundredweight of cabbage. They are real monuments of green stuff.

Later, man thought of obtaining a generous dish with the thousand little sprays of the inflorescence. The cabbage consented. Under the cover of the central leaves, it gorged with food its sheaves of blossom, its flower-stalks, its branches and worked the lot into a fleshy conglomeration. This is the cauliflower, the broccoli.

Differently entreated, the plant, economizing in the centre of its shoot, set a whole family of closs-wrapped cabbages ladder-wise on a tall stem. A multitude of dwarf leaf-buds took the place of the colossal head. This is the Brussels sprout.

Next comes the turn of the stump, an unprofitable, almost wooden thing, which seemed never to have any other purpose than to act as a support for the plant. But the tricks of gardeners are capable of everything, so much so that the stalk yields to the grower's suggestions and becomes fleshy and swells into an ellipse similar to the turnip, of which it possesses all the merits of corpulence,

The Cabbage-caterpillar

flavour and delicacy; only the strange product serves as a base for a few sparse leaves, the last protests of a real stem that refuses to lose its attributes entirely. This is the cole-rape.

If the stem allows itself to be allured, why not the root? It does in fact, yield to the blandishments of agriculture: it dilates its pivot into a flat turnip, which half emerges from the ground. This is the rutabaga, or swede, the turnip-cabbage of our northern districts.

Incomparably docile under our nursing, the cabbage has given its all for our nourishment and that of our cattle: its leaves, its flowers, its buds, its stalk, its root; all that it now wants is to combine the ornamental with the useful, to smarten itself, to adorn our flower-beds and cut a good figure on a drawing-room table. It has done this to perfection, not with its flowers, which, in their modesty, continue intractible, but with its curly and variegated leaves, which have the undulating grace of Ostrich-feathers and the rich colouring of a mixed bouquet. None who beholds it in this magnificence will recognize the near relation

333

of the vulgar "greens" that form the basis of our cabbage-soup.

The cabbage, first in order of date in our kitchen-gardens, was held in high esteem by classic antiquity, next after the bean and, later, the pea; but it goes much farther back, so far indeed that no memories of its acquisition remain. History pays but little attention to these details: it celebrates the battle-fields whereon we meet our death, it scorns to speak of the ploughed fields whereby we thrive; it knows the names of the kings' bastards, it cannot tell us the origin of wheat. That is the way of human folly.

This silence respecting the precious plants that serve as food is most regrettable. The cabbage in particular, the venerable cabbage, that denizen of the most ancient garden-plots, would have had extremely interesting things to teach us. It is a treasure in itself, but a treasure twice exploited, first by man and next by the caterpillar of the Pieris, the common Large White Butterfly whom we all know *(Pieris brassicæ,* LIN.*)*. This caterpillar feeds indiscriminately on the leaves of all varieties of cabbage, however dissimilar in appearance: he nibbles with the same ap-

The Cabbage-caterpillar

petite red cabbage and broccoli, curly greens and savoy, swedes and turnip-tops, in short, all that our ingenuity, lavish of time and patience, has been able to obtain from the original plant since the most distant ages.

But what did the caterpillar eat before our cabbages supplied him with copious provender? Obviously the Pieris did not wait for the advent of man and his horticultural works in order to take part in the joys of life. She lived without us and would have continued to live without us. A Butterfly's existence is not subject to ours, but rightfully independent of our aid.

Before the white-heart, the cauliflower, the savoy and the others were invented, the Pieris' caterpillar certainly did not lack food: he browsed the wild cabbage of the cliffs, the parent of all the latter-day wealth; but, as this plant is not widely distributed and is, in any case, limited to certain maritime regions, the welfare of the Butterfly, whether on plain or hill, demanded a more luxuriant and more common plant for pasturage. This plant was apparently one of the Cruciferæ, more or less seasoned with sulphuretted essence, like the cabbages. Let us experiment on these lines.

The Life of the Caterpillar

I rear the Pieris' caterpillars from the egg
upwards on the wall-rocket (*Diplotaxis tenui-
folia*, DEC.), which imbibes strong spices
along the edge of the paths and at the foot of
the walls. Penned in a large, wire-gauze bell-
cage, they accept this provender without de-
mur; they nibble it with the same appetite as
if it were cabbage; and they end by producing
chrysalids and Butterflies. The change of fare
causes not the least trouble.

I am equally successful with other crucifers
of a less marked flavour: white mustard
(Sinapis incana, LIN.), dyer's woad *(Isatis
tinctoria*, LIN.), wild radish *(Raphanus
raphanistrum*, LIN.), whitlow pepperwort
(Lepidium draba, LIN.), hedge-mustard
(Sisymbrium officinale, SCOP.). On the other
hand, the leaves of the lettuce, the bean, the
pea, the corn-salad are obstinately refused.
Let us be content with what we have seen:
the fare has been sufficiently varied to show
us that the Cabbage-caterpillar feeds exclusively on a large number of crucifers, perhaps
even on all.

As these experiments are made in the enclosure of a bell-cage, one might imagine that
captivity impels the flock to feed, in the

The Cabbage-caterpillar

absence of better things, on what it would refuse were it free to hunt for itself. Having naught else within their reach, the starvelings consume any and all Cruciferæ, without distinction of species. Can things sometimes be the same in the open fields, where I play none of my tricks? Can the family of the White Butterfly be settled on other crucifers than the cabbage? I start a quest along the paths near the gardens and end by finding on wild radish and white mustard colonies as crowded and prosperous as those established on cabbage.

Now, except when the metamorphosis is at hand, the caterpillar of the White Butterfly never travels: he does all his growing on the identical plant whereon he saw the light. The caterpillars observed on the wild radish, as well as other households, are not, therefore, emigrants who have come as a matter of fancy from some cabbage-patch in the neighbourhood: they have hatched on the very leaves where I find them. Hence I arrive at this conclusion: the White Butterfly, who is fitful in her flight, chooses cabbage first, to dab her eggs upon, and different Cruciferæ next, varying greatly in appearance.

The Life of the Caterpillar

How does the Pieris manage to know her
way about her botanical domain? We have
seen the Larini,[1] those explorers of fleshy
receptacles with an artichoke flavour, astonish
us with their knowledge of the flora of the
thistle tribe; but their lore might, at a pinch,
be explained by the method followed at the
moment of housing the egg. With their
rostrum, they prepare niches and dig out
basins in the receptacle exploited and consequently they taste the thing a little before
entrusting their eggs to it. On the other
hand, the Butterfly, a nectar-drinker, makes
not the least enquiry into the savoury qualities
of the leafage; at most, dipping her proboscis
into the flowers, she abstracts a mouthful of
syrup. This means of investigation, moreover, would be of no use to her, for the plant
selected for the establishing of her family is,
for the most part, not yet in flower. The
mother flits for a moment around the plant;
and that swift examination is enough: the
emission of eggs takes place if the provender
be found suitable.

The botanist, to recognize a crucifer, re-

[1] A species of Weevils found on thistle-heads.—*Translator's Note.*

338

quires the indications provided by the flower.
Here the Pieris surpasses us. She does not
consult the seed-vessel, to see if it be long or
short, nor yet the petals, four in number and
arranged in a cross, because the plant, as a
rule, is not in flower; and still she recognizes
off-hand what suits her caterpillars, in spite
of profound differences that would embarrass
any but a botanical expert.

Unless the Pieris has an innate power of
discrimination to guide her, it is impossible
to understand the great extent of her vegetable
realm. She needs for her family Cruciferæ,
nothing but Cruciferæ; and she knows this
group of plants to perfection. I have been an
enthusiastic botanist for half a century and
more. Nevertheless, to discover if this or
that plant, new to me, is or is not one of the
Cruciferæ, in the absence of flowers and fruits
I should have more faith in the Butterfly's
statements than in all the learned records of
the books. Where science is apt to make
mistakes, instinct is infallible.

The Pieris has two families a year: one in
April and May, the other in September. The
cabbage-patches are renewed in those same
months. The Butterfly's calendar tallies with

the gardener's: the moment that provisions
are in sight, consumers are forthcoming for
the feast.

The eggs are a bright orange-yellow and
do not lack prettiness when examined under
the lens. They are blunted cones, ranged side
by side on their round base and adorned with
finely-scored longitudinal ridges. They are
collected in slabs, sometimes on the upper
surface, when the leaf that serves as a support is spread wide, sometimes on the lower
surface when the leaf is pressed to the next
ones. Their number varies considerably.
Slabs of a couple of hundred are pretty frequent; isolated eggs, or eggs collected in small
groups, are, on the contrary, rare. The
mother's output is affected by the degree of
quietness at the moment of laying.

The outer circumference of the group is
irregularly formed, but the inside presents a
certain order. The eggs are here arranged
in straight rows backing against one another
in such a way that each egg finds a double
support in the preceding row. This alternation, without being of an irreproachable
precision, gives a fairly stable equilibrium to
the whole.

The Cabbage-caterpillar

To see the mother at her laying is no easy matter: when examined too closely, the Pieris decamps at once. The structure of the work, however, reveals the order of the operations pretty clearly. The ovipositor swings slowly first in this direction, then in that, by turns; and a new egg is lodged in each space between two adjoining eggs in the previous row. The extent of the oscillation determines the length of the row, which is longer or shorter according to the layer's fancy.

The hatching takes place in about a week. It is almost simultaneous for the whole mass: as soon as one caterpillar comes out of its egg, the others come out also, as though the natal impulse were communicated from one to the other. In the same way, in the nest of the Praying Mantis, a warning seems to be spread abroad, arousing every one of the population. It is a wave propagated in all directions from the point first struck.

The egg does not open by means of a dehiscence similar to that of the vegetable-pods whose seeds have attained maturity; it is the new-born grub itself that contrives an exit-way by gnawing a hole in its enclosure. In this manner, it obtains near the top of the cone a symmetrical dormer-window, clean-edged, with no joins nor unevenness of any kind, showing that this part of the wall has been nibbled away and swallowed. But for this breach, which is just wide enough for the deliverance, the egg remains intact, standing firmly on its base. It is now that the lens is best able to take in its elegant structure. What it sees is a bag made of ultra-fine gold-beater's-skin, translucent, stiff and white, retaining the complete form of the original egg. A score of streaked and knotted lines run from the top to the base. It is the wizard's pointed cap, the mitre with the grooves carved into jewelled chaplets. All said, the Cabbage-caterpillar's birth-casket is an exquisite work of art.

The hatching of the lot is finished in a couple of hours and the swarming family musters on the layer of swaddling-clothes, still in the same position. For a long time, before descending to the fostering leaf, it lingers on this kind of hot-bed, is even very busy there. Busy with what? It is browsing a strange kind of grass, the handsome mitres that remain standing on end. Slowly and methodically, from top to base, the new-born

The Cabbage-caterpillar

grubs nibble the wallets whence they have just
emerged. By to-morrow, nothing is left of
these but a pattern of round dots, the bases
of the vanished sacks.

As his first mouthfuls, therefore, the Cabbage-caterpillar eats the membranous wrapper
of his egg. This is a regulation diet, for I
have never seen one of the little grubs allow
itself to be tempted by the adjacent green
stuff before finishing the ritual repast whereat
skin bottles furnish forth the feast. It is the
first time that I have seen a larva make a meal
of the sack in which it was born. Of what
use can this singular fare be to the budding
caterpillar? I suspect as follows: the leaves of
the cabbage are waxed and slippery surfaces
and nearly always slant considerably. To
graze on them without risking a fall, which
would be fatal in earliest childhood, is hardly
possible unless with moorings that afford a
steady support. What is needed is bits of silk
stretched along the road as fast as progress is
made, something for the legs to grip, something to provide a good anchorage even when
the grub is upside down. The silk-tubes,
where those moorings are manufactured, must
be very scantily supplied in a tiny, new-born

animal; and it is expedient that they be filled without delay with the aid of a special form of nourishment. Then what shall the nature of the first food be? Vegetable matter, slow to elaborate and niggardly in its yield, does not fulfil the desired conditions at all well, for time presses and we must trust ourselves safely to the slippery leaf. An animal diet would be preferable: it is easier to digest and undergoes chemical changes in a shorter time. The wrapper of the egg is of a horny nature, as silk itself is. It will not take long to transform the one into the other. The grub therefore tackles the remains of its egg and turns it into silk to carry with it on its first journeys.

If my surmise is well-founded, there is reason to believe that, with a view to speedily filling the silk-glands to which they look to supply them with ropes, other caterpillars beginning their existence on smooth and steeply-slanting leaves also take as their first mouthful the membranous sack which is all that remains of the egg.

The whole of the platform of birth-sacks which was the first camping-ground of the White Butterfly's family is razed to the ground; naught remains but the round marks

The Cabbage-caterpillar

of the individual pieces that composed it. The structure of piles has disappeared; the prints left by the piles remain. The little caterpillars are now on the level of the leaf which shall henceforth feed them. They are a pale orange-yellow, with a sprinkling of white bristles. The head is a shiny black and remarkably powerful; it already gives signs of the coming gluttony. The little animal measures scarcely two millimetres[1] in length.

The troop begins its steadying-work as soon as it comes into contact with its pasturage, the green cabbage-leaf. Here, there, in its immediate neighbourhood, each grub emits from its spinning-glands short cables so slender that it takes an attentive lens to catch a glimpse of them. This is enough to ensure the equilibrium of the almost imponderable atom.

The vegetarian meal now begins. The grub's length promptly increases from two millimetres to four. Soon, a moult takes place which alters its costume: its skin becomes speckled, on a pale-yellow ground, with a number of black dots intermingled with white bristles. Three or four days of rest are necessary after the fatigue of breaking cover.

[1] .078 inch.—*Translator's Note.*

The Life of the Caterpillar

When this is over, the hunger-fit starts that
will make a ruin of the cabbage within a few
weeks.

What an appetite! What a stomach, working continuously day and night! It is a
devouring laboratory, through which the
foodstuffs merely pass, transformed at once.
I serve up to my caged herd a bunch of
leaves picked from among the biggest: two
hours later, nothing remains but the thick
midribs; and even these are attacked when
there is any delay in renewing the victuals.
At this rate, a "hundredweight-cabbage,"
doled out leaf by leaf, would not last my
menagerie a week.

The gluttonous animal, therefore, when it
swarms and multiplies, is a scourge. How
are we to protect our gardens against it? In
the days of Pliny, the great Latin naturalist,
a stake was set up in the middle of the cabbage-bed to be preserved; and on this stake
was fixed a Horse's skull bleached in the sun:
a Mare's skull was considered even better.
This sort of bogey was supposed to ward off
the devouring brood.

My confidence in this preservative is but an
indifferent one; my reason for mentioning it

The Cabbage-caterpillar

is that it reminds me of a custom still observed in our own days, at least in my part of the country. Nothing is so long-lived as absurdity. Tradition has retained, in a simplified form, the ancient defensive apparatus of which Pliny speaks. For the Horse's skull our people have substituted an eggshell on the top of a switch stuck among the cabbages. It is easier to arrange; also, it is quite as useful, that is to say, it has no effect whatever.

Everything, even the nonsensical, is capable of explanation with a little credulity. When I question the peasants, our neighbours, they tell me that the effect of the eggshell is as simple as can be: the Butterflies, attracted by the whiteness, come and lay their eggs on it. Broiled by the sun and lacking all nourishment on that thankless support, the little caterpillars die; and that makes so many fewer.

I insist; I ask them if they have ever seen slabs of eggs or masses of young caterpillars on those white shells.

"Never," they reply, with one voice.

"Well, then?"

"It was done in the old days and so we go on doing it: that's all we know; and that's enough for us."

The Life of the Caterpillar

I leave it at that, persuaded that the memory of the Horse's skull used once upon a time is ineradicable, like all the rustic absurdities implanted by the ages.

We have, when all is said, but one means of protection, which is to watch and inspect the cabbage-leaves assiduously and crush the slabs of eggs between our finger and thumb and the caterpillars with our feet. Nothing is so effective as this method, which makes great demands on one's time and vigilance. What pains to obtain an unspoilt cabbage! And what a debt do we not owe to those humble scrapers of the soil, those ragged heroes who provide us with the wherewithal to live!

To eat and digest, to accumulate reserves whence the Butterfly will issue: that is the caterpillar's one and only business. The Cabbage-caterpillar performs it with insatiable gluttony. Incessantly it browses, incessantly digests: the supreme felicity of an animal which is little more than an intestine. There is never a distraction, unless it be certain see-saw movements which are particularly curious when several caterpillars are grazing side by side, abreast. Then, at intervals, all the heads

The Cabbage-caterpillar

in the row are briskly lifted and as briskly lowered, time after time, with an automatic precision worthy of a Prussian drill-ground. Can it be their method of intimidating an always possible aggressor? Can it be a manifestation of gaiety, when the wanton sun warms their full paunches? Whether sign of fear or sign of bliss, this is the only exercise that the gluttons allow themselves until the proper degree of plumpness is attained.

After a month's grazing, the voracious appetite of my caged herd is assuaged. The caterpillars climb the trelliswork in every direction, walk about anyhow, with their forepart raised and searching space. Here and there, as they pass, the swaying herd put forth a thread. They wander restlessly, anxiously to travel afar. The exodus now prevented by the trellised enclosure I once saw under excellent conditions. At the advent of the cold weather, I had placed a few cabbage-stalks, covered with caterpillars, in a small greenhouse. Those who saw the common kitchen vegetable sumptuously lodged under glass, in the company of the pelargonium and the Chinese primrose, were astonished at my curious fancy. I let them smile. I had my

349

plans: I wanted to find out how the family of the Large White Butterfly behaves when the cold weather sets in. Things happened just as I wished. At the end of November, the caterpillars, having grown to the desired extent, left the cabbages, one by one, and began to roam about the walls. None of them fixed himself there or made preparations for the transformation. I suspected that they wanted the choice of a spot in the open air, exposed to all the rigours of winter. I therefore left the door of the hothouse open. Soon, the whole crowd had disappeared.

I found them dispersed all over the neighbouring walls, some thirty yards off. The thrust of a ledge, the eaves formed by a projecting bit of mortar served them as a shelter where the chrysalid moult took place and where the winter was passed. The Cabbage-caterpillar possesses a robust constitution, unsusceptible to torrid heat or icy cold. All that he needs for his metamorphosis is an airy lodging, free from permanent damp.

The inmates of my fold, therefore, move about for a few days on the trelliswork, anxious to travel afar in search of a wall. Finding none and realizing that time presses,

The Cabbage-caterpillar

they resign themselves. Each one, supporting himself on the trellis, first weaves around himself a thin carpet of white silk, which will form the sustaining layer at the time of the laborious and delicate work of the nymphosis. He fixes his rear-end to this base by a silk pad and his fore-part by a strap that passes under his shoulders and is fixed on either side to the carpet. Thus slung from his three fastenings, he strips himself of his larval apparel and turns into a chrysalis in the open air, with no protection save that of the wall, which the caterpillar would certainly have found had I not interfered.

Of a surety, he would be short-sighted indeed that pictured a world of good things prepared exclusively for our advantage. The earth, the great foster-mother, has a generous breast. At the very moment when nourishing matter is created, even though it be with our own zealous aid, she summons to the feast host upon host of consumers, who are all the more numerous and enterprising in proportion as the table is more amply spread. The cherry of our orchards is excellent eating: a maggot contends with us for its possession. In vain do we weigh suns and planets: our supremacy,

351

The Life of the Caterpillar

which fathoms the universe, cannot prevent a wretched worm from levying its toll on the delicious fruit. We make ourselves at home in a cabbage-bed: the sons of the Pieris make themselves at home there too. Preferring broccoli to wild radish, they profit where we have profited; and we have no remedy against their competition save caterpillar-raids and egg-crushing, a thankless, tedious and none too efficacious work.

Every creature has its claims on life. The Cabbage-caterpillar eagerly puts forth his own, so much so that the cultivation of the precious plant would be endangered if others concerned did not take part in its defence. These others are the auxiliaries,[1] our helpers from necessity and not from sympathy. The words friend and foe, auxiliaries and ravagers are here the mere conventions of a language not always adapted to render the exact truth. He is our foe who eats or attacks our crops; our friend is he who feeds upon our foes. Everything is reduced to a frenzied contest of appetites.

[1] The author employs this word to denote the insects that are helpful, while describing as "ravagers" the insects that are hurtful to the farmer's crops.—*Translator's Note.*

The Cabbage-caterpillar

In the name of the might that is mine, of
trickery, of highway robbery, clear out of
that, you, and make room for me: give me
your seat at the banquet! That is the inex-
orable law in the world of animals and more
or less, alas, in our own world as well!

Now, among our entomological auxiliaries,
the smallest in size are the best at their work.
One of them is charged with watching over
the cabbages. She is so small, she works so
discreetly that the gardener does not know
her, has not even heard of her. Were he to
see her by accident, flitting around the plant
which she protects, he would take no notice
of her, would not suspect the service rendered.
I propose to set forth the tiny midget's
deserts.

Scientists call her *Microgaster glomeratus*.
What exactly was in the mind of the author
of the name Microgaster, which means little
belly? Did he intend to allude to the insig-
nificance of the abdomen? Not so. However slight the belly may be, the insect nevertheless possesses one, correctly proportioned
to the rest of the body, so that the classic denomination, far from giving us any information, might mislead us, were we to trust it

353

wholly. Nomenclature, which changes from day to day and becomes more and more cacophonous, is an unsafe guide. Instead of asking the animal what its name is, let us begin by asking:

"What can you do? What is your business?"

Well, the Microgaster's business is to exploit the Cabbage-caterpillar, a clearly-defined business, admitting of no possible confusion. Would we behold her works? In the spring, let us inspect the neighbourhood of the kitchen-garden. Be our eye never so unobservant, we shall notice against the walls or on the withered grasses at the foot of the hedges some very small yellow cocoons, heaped into masses the size of a hazel-nut. Beside each group lies a Cabbage-caterpillar, sometimes dying, sometimes dead and always presenting a most tattered appearance. These cocoons are the work of the Microgaster's family, hatched or on the point of hatching into the perfect stage; the caterpillar is the dish whereon that family has fed during its larval state. The epithet *glomeratus*, which accompanies the name of Microgaster, suggests this conglomeration of cocoons. Let us

354

The Cabbage-caterpillar

collect the clusters as they are, without seeking
to separate them, an operation which would
demand both patience and dexterity, for the
cocoons are closely united by the inextricable
tangle of their surface-threads. In May, a
swarm of pigmies will sally forth, ready to
get to business in the cabbages.

Colloquial language uses the terms Midge
and Gnat to describe the tiny insects which we
often see dancing in a ray of sunlight. There
is something of everything in those aerial bal-
lets. It is possible that the persecutrix of the
Cabbage-caterpillar is there, along with many
another; but the name of Midge cannot properly be applied to her. He who says Midge
says Fly, Dipteron, two-winged insect; and
our friend has four wings, one and all
adapted for flying. By virtue of this characteristic and others no less important, she belongs to the order of Hymenoptera.[1] No
matter: as our language possesses no more
precise term outside the scientific vocabulary,
let us use the expression Midge, which pretty
well conveys the general idea. Our Midge,
the Microgaster, is the size of an average

[1]This order includes the Ichneumon-flies, of whom the
Microgaster is one.—*Translator's Note.*

355

The Life of the Caterpillar

Gnat. She measures 3 or 4 millimetres.[1] The two sexes are equally numerous and wear the same costume, a black uniform, all but the legs, which are pale red. In spite of this likeness, they are easily distinguished. The male has an abdomen which is slightly flattened and moreover curved at the tip; the female, before the laying, has hers full and perceptibly distended by its ovular contents. This rapid sketch of the insect should be enough for our purpose.

If we wish to know the grub and especially to inform ourselves of its manner of living, it is advisable to rear in a cage a numerous herd of Cabbage-caterpillars. Whereas a direct search on the cabbages in our garden would give us but a difficult and uncertain harvest, by this means we shall daily have as many as we wish before our eyes.

In the course of June, which is the time when the caterpillars quit their pastures and go far afield to settle on some wall or other, those in my fold, finding nothing better, climb to the dome of the cage to make their preparations and to spin a supporting network for the chrysalid's needs. Among these spin-

[1] .117 to .156 inch.—*Translator's Note.*

The Cabbage-caterpillar

ners we see some weaklings working listlessly
at their carpet. Their appearance makes us
deem them in the grip of a mortal disease.
I take a few of them and open their bellies,
using a needle by way of a scalpel. What
comes out is a bunch of green entrails, soaked
in a bright yellow fluid, which is really the
creature's blood. These tangled intestines
swarm with little, lazy grubs, varying greatly
in number, from ten or twenty at least to
sometimes half-a-hundred. They are the offspring of the Microgaster.

What do they feed on? The lens makes
conscientious enquiries; nowhere does it manage to show me the vermin attacking solid
nourishment, fatty tissues, muscles or other
parts; nowhere do I see them bite, gnaw or
dissect. The following experiment will tell
us more fully: I pour into a watch-glass the
crowds extracted from the hospitable paunches. I flood them with caterpillar's blood
obtained by simple pricks; I place the preparation under a glass bell-jar, in a moist
atmosphere, to prevent evaporation; I repeat
the nourishing bath by means of fresh bleed-
ings and give them the stimulant which they
would have gained from the living caterpillar.

The Life of the Caterpillar

Thanks to these precautions, my charges have all the appearance of excellent health; they drink and thrive. But this state of things cannot last long. Soon ripe for the transformation, my grubs leave the dining-room of the watch-glass as they would have left the caterpillar's belly; they come to the ground to try and weave their tiny cocoons. They fail in the attempt and perish. They have missed a suitable support, that is to say, the silky carpet provided by the dying caterpillar. No matter: I have seen enough to convince me. The larvæ of the Microgaster do not eat in the strict sense of the word: they live on soup; and that soup is the caterpillar's blood.

Examine the parasites closely and you shall see that their diet is bound to be a liquid one. They are little white grubs, neatly segmented, with a pointed fore-part splashed with tiny black marks, as though the atom had been slaking its thirst in a drop of ink. It moves its hind-quarters slowly, without shifting its position. I place it under the microscope. The mouth is a pore, devoid of any apparatus for disintegration-work: it has no fangs, no horny nippers, no mandibles; its attack is just

The Cabbage-caterpillar

a kiss. It does not chew, it sucks, it takes discreet sips at the moisture all around it.

The fact that it refrains entirely from biting is confirmed by my autopsy of the stricken caterpillars. In the patient's belly, notwithstanding the number of nurselings who hardly leave room for the nurse's entrails, everything is in perfect order; nowhere do we see a trace of mutilation. Nor does aught on the outside betray any havoc within. The exploited caterpillars graze and move about peacefully, giving no sign of pain. It is impossible for me to distinguish them from the unscathed ones in respect of appetite and untroubled digestion.

When the time approaches to weave the carpet for the support of the chrysalis, an appearance of emaciation at last points to the evil that is at their vitals. They spin nevertheless. They are stoics who do not forget their duty in the hour of death. At last, they expire, quite softly, not of any wounds, but of anæmia, even as a lamp goes out when the oil comes to an end. And it has to be. The living caterpillar, capable of feeding itself and forming blood, is a necessity for the welfare of the grubs; it has to last about a month, until the Microgaster's offspring have achieved their full growth. The two calendars synchronize in a remarkable way. When the caterpillar leaves off eating and makes its preparations for the metamorphosis, the parasites are ripe for the exodus. The bottle dries up when the drinkers cease to need it; but until that moment it must remain more or less well-filled, although becoming limper daily. It is important, therefore, that the caterpillar's existence be not endangered by wounds which, even though very tiny, would stop the working of the blood-fountains. With this intent, the drainers of the bottle are, in a manner of speaking, muzzled; they have by way of a mouth a pore that sucks without bruising.

The dying caterpillar continues to lay the silk of his carpet with a slow oscillation of the head. The moment now comes for the parasites to emerge. This happens in June and generally at nightfall. A breach is made on the ventral surface or else in the sides, never on the back: one breach only, contrived at a point of minor resistance, at the junction of two segments; for it is bound to be a toilsome business, in the absence of a set of filing-tools.

The Cabbage-caterpillar

Perhaps the worms take one another's places at the point attacked and come by turns to work at it with a kiss.

In one short spell, the whole tribe issues through this single opening and is soon wriggling about, perched on the surface of the caterpillar. The lens cannot perceive the hole, which closes on the instant. There is not even a hæmorrhage: the bottle has been drained too thoroughly. You must press it between your fingers to squeeze out a few drops of moisture and thus discover the spot of exit.

Around the caterpillar, who is not always quite dead and who sometimes even goes on weaving his carpet a moment longer, the vermin at once begin to work at their cocoons. The straw-coloured thread, drawn from the silk-glands by a backward jerk of the head, is first fixed to the white network of the caterpillar and then produces adjacent warp-beams, so that, by mutual entanglements, the individual works are welded together and form an agglomeration in which each of the worms has its own cabin. For the moment, what is woven is not the real cocoon, but a general scaffolding which will facilitate the construc-

tion of the separate shells. All these frames
rest upon those adjoining and, mixing up their
threads, become a common edifice wherein
each grub contrives a shelter for itself. Here
at last the real cocoon is spun, a pretty little
piece of closely-woven work.

In my rearing-jars, I obtain as many groups
of those tiny shells as my future experiments
can wish for. Three-fourths of the caterpillars have supplied me with them, so ruthless
has been the toll of the spring births. I lodge
these groups, one by one, in separate glass
tubes, thus forming a collection on which I
can draw at will, while, in view of my experiments, I keep under observation the whole
swarm produced by one caterpillar.

The adult Microgaster appears a fortnight
later, in the middle of June. There are fifty
in the first tube examined. The riotous multitude is in the full enjoyment of the pairing-
season, for the two sexes always figure among
the guests of any one caterpillar. What
animation! What an orgy of love! The
carnival of those pigmies bewilders the observer and makes his head swim.

Most of the females, wishful of liberty,
plunge down to the waist between the glass of

The Cabbage-caterpillar

the tube and the plug of cotton-wool that closes the end turned to the light; but the lower halves remain free and form a circular gallery in front of which the males hustle one another, take one another's places and hastily operate. Each bides his turn, each attends to his little matters for a few moments and then makes way for his rivals and goes off to start again elsewhere. The turbulent wedding lasts all the morning and begins afresh next day, a mighty throng of couples embracing, separating and embracing once more.

There is every reason to believe that, in gardens, the mated ones, finding themselves in isolated couples, would keep quieter. Here, in the tube, things degenerate into a riot because the assembly is too numerous for the narrow space.

What is lacking to complete its happiness? Apparently, a little food, a few sugary mouthfuls extracted from the flowers. I serve up some provisions in the tubes: not drops of honey, in which the puny creatures would get stuck, but little strips of paper spread with that dainty. They come to them, take their stand on them and refresh themselves. The fare appears to agree with them. With this diet, renewed as the strips dry up, I can keep them in very good condition until the end of my inquisition.

There is another arrangement to be made. The colonists in my spare tubes are restless and quick of flight; they will have to be transferred presently to sundry vessels without my risking the loss of a good number, or even the whole lot, a loss which my hands, my forceps and other means of coercion would be unable to prevent by checking the nimble movements of the tiny prisoners. The irresistible attraction of the sunlight comes to my aid. If I lay one of my tubes horizontally on the table, turning one end towards the full light of a sunny window, the captives at once make for this brighter end and play about there for a long while, without seeking to retreat. If I turn the tube in the opposite direction, the crowd immediately shifts its quarters and collects at the other end. The brilliant sunlight is its great joy. With this bait, I can send it whithersoever I please.

We will therefore place the new receptacle, jar or test-tube, on the table, pointing the closed end towards the window. At its mouth, we open one of the full tubes. No other precaution is needed: even though the mouth leaves a large interval free, the swarm hastens into the lighted chamber. All that remains to be done is to close the apparatus before moving it. The observer is now in control of the multitude, without appreciable losses, and is able to question it at will.

We will begin by asking:

"How do you manage to lodge your germs inside the caterpillar?"

This question and others of the same category, which ought to take precedence of everything else, are generally neglected by the impaler of insects, who cares more for the niceties of nomenclature than for glorious realities. He classifies his subjects, dividing them into regiments with barbarous labels, a work which seems to him the highest expression of entomological science. Names, nothing but names: the rest hardly counts. The persecutor of the Pieris used to be called Microgaster, that is to say, little belly: to-day she is called Apantales, that is to say, the incomplete. What a fine step forward! We now know all about it!

Can our friend at least tell us how "the little belly" or "the incomplete" gets into the

The Life of the Caterpillar

caterpillar? Not a bit of it! A book which, judging by its recent date, should be the faithful echo of our actual knowledge, informs us that the Microgaster inserts her eggs direct into the caterpillar's body. It goes on to say that the parasitic vermin inhabit the chrysalis, whence they make their way out by perforating the stout horny wrapper. Hundreds of times have I witnessed the exodus of the grubs ripe for weaving their cocoons; and the exit has always been made through the skin of the caterpillar and never through the armour of the chrysalis. The fact that its mouth is a mere clinging pore, deprived of any offensive weapon, would even lead me to believe that the grub is incapable of perforating the chrysalid's covering.

This proved error makes me doubt the other proposition, though logical, after all, and agreeing with the methods followed by a host of parasites. No matter: my faith in what I read in print is of the slightest; I perfer to go straight to facts. Before making a statement of any kind, I want to see, what I call seeing. It is a slower and more laborious process; but it is certainly much safer.

I will not undertake to lie in wait for what

The Cabbage-caterpillar

takes place on the cabbages in the garden:
that method is too uncertain and besides does
not lend itself to precise observation. As I
have in hand the necessary materials, to wit,
my collection of tubes swarming with the
parasites newly hatched into the adult form,
I will operate on the little table in my animals'
laboratory. A jar with a capacity of about a
litre[1] is placed on the table, with the bottom
turned towards the window in the sun. I put
into it a cabbage-leaf covered with caterpillars, sometimes fully developed, sometimes
half-way, sometimes just out of the egg. A
strip of honeyed paper will serve the Microgaster as a dining-room, if the experiment is
destined to take some time. Lastly, by the
method of transfer which I described above,
I send the inmates of one of my tubes into
the apparatus. Once the jar is closed, there
is nothing left to do but to let things take
their course and to keep an assiduous watch,
for days and weeks, if need be. Nothing
worth remarking can escape me.

The caterpillars graze placidly, heedless of
their terrible attendants. If some giddy-pates
in the turbulent swarm pass over the caterpil-

[1]About 1¾ pints, or .22 gallon.—*Translator's Note.*

lars' spines, these draw up their fore-part with
a jerk and as suddenly lower it again; and
that is all: the intruders forthwith decamp.
Nor do the latter seem to contemplate any
harm: they refresh themselves on the honey-
smeared strip, they come and go tumultuously.
Their short flights may land them, now in
one place, now in another, on the browsing
herd, but they pay no attention to it. What
we see is casual meetings, not deliberate en-
counters.

In vain I change the flock of caterpillars
and vary their age; in vain I change the squad
of parasites: in vain I follow events in the
jar for long hours, morning and evening, both
in a dim light and in the full glare of the sun:
I succeed in seeing nothing, absolutely nothing, on the parasite's side, that resembles
an attack. No matter what the ill-informed
authors say—ill-informed because they had
not the patience to see for themselves—the
conclusion at which I arrive is positive: to
inject the germs, the Microgaster never attacks the caterpillars.

The invasion, therefore, is necessarily effected through the Butterfly's eggs themselves, as experiment will prove. My broad

jar would tell against the inspection of the troop, kept at too great a distance by the glass enclosure; and I therefore select a tube an inch wide. I place in this a shred of cabbage-leaf, bearing a slab of eggs, as laid by the Butter-fly. I next introduce the inmates of one of my spare vessels. A strip of paper smeared with honey accompanies the new arrivals.

This happens early in July. Soon, the females are there, fussing about, sometimes to the extent of blackening the whole slab of yellow eggs. They inspect the treasure, flutter their wings and brush their hind-legs against each other, a sign of keen satisfaction. They sound the heap, probe the interstices with their antennæ and tap the individual eggs with their palpi; then, this one here, that one there, they quickly apply the tip of their abdomen to the egg selected. Each time, we see a slender, horny prickle darting from the ventral surface, close to the end. This is the instrument that deposits the germ under the film of the egg; it is the inoculation-needle. The operation is performed calmly and methodically, even when several mothers are working at one and the same time. Where one has been, a second goes, followed by a third, a fourth and others yet, nor am I able definitely to see the end of the visits paid to the same egg. Each time, the needle enters and inserts a germ.

It is impossible, in such a crowd, for the eye to follow the successive mothers who hasten to lay in each; but there is one quite practicable method by which we can estimate the number of germs introduced into a single egg, which is, later, to open the ravaged caterpillars and count the worms which they contain. A less repugnant means is to number the little cocoons heaped up around each dead caterpillar. The total will tell us how many germs were injected, some by the same mother returning several times to the egg already treated, others by different mothers. Well, the number of these cocoons varies greatly. Generally, it fluctuates in the neighbourhood of twenty, but I have come across as many as sixty-five; and nothing tells me that this is the extreme limit. What hideous industry for the extermination of a Butterfly's progeny!

I am fortunate at this moment in having a highly-cultured visitor, versed in the profundities of philosophic thought. I make way

The Cabbage-caterpillar

for him before the apparatus wherein the
Microgaster is at work. For an hour and
more, standing lens in hand, he, in his turn,
looks and sees what I have just seen; he
watches the layers who go from one egg to the
other, make their choice, draw their slender
lancet and prick what the stream of passers-
by, one after the other, have already pricked.
Thoughtful and a little uneasy, he puts down
his lens at last. Never had he been vouch-
safed so clear a glimpse as here, in my finger-
wide tube, of the masterly brigandage that
runs through all life down to that of the very
smallest.

INDEX

373

Index

374

Index

Index

On the following pages will be found the complete list of titles in " The Modern Library," including recent new titles. New titles are added in the Spring and Fall of every year.

Complete List of Titles in
THE MODERN LIBRARY

For convenience in ordering please use number at right of title

A MODERN BOOK OF CRITICISMS (81) Edited with an
Introduction by LUDWIG LEWISOHN
ANDERSON, SHERWOOD (1876-   )
Winesburg, Ohio (104)
ANDREYEV, LEONID (1871-   )
The Seven That Were Hanged and The Red Laugh (45)
Introduction by THOMAS SELTZER
ATHERTON, GERTRUDE (1859-   )
Rezanov (71) Introduction by WILLIAM MARION REEDY
BALZAC, HONORE DE (1799-1850)
Short Stories (40) Edited by T. R. SMITH
BAUDELAIRE, PIERRE CHARLES (1821-1867)
His Prose and Poetry (70) Edited by T. R. SMITH. Intro-
duction by ARTHUR SYMONS
BEARDSLEY, AUBREY, THE ART OF (1872-1898)
64 Black and White Reproductions (42)
Introduction by ARTHUR SYMONS
BEST GHOST STORIES (73)
Introduction by ARTHUR B. REEVE
BEST HUMOROUS AMERICAN SHORT STORIES (87)
Edited with an Introduction by ALEXANDER JESSUP
BEST RUSSIAN SHORT STORIES (18)
Edited with an Introduction by THOMAS SELTZER
BLAKE, WILLIAM (1757-1827)
Poems (91)
Edited with notes by WILLIAM BUTLER YEATS
BUTLER, SAMUEL (1835-1902)
The Way of All Flesh (13)
CABELL, JAMES BRANCH
Beyond Life (25) Introduction by GUY HOLT
CARPENTER, EDWARD (1844-   )
Love's Coming of Age (51)
CARROLL, LEWIS
Alice in Wonderland, Through the Looking Glass, and The
Hunting of the Snark (79)
Introduction by ALEXANDER WOOLLCOTT
CHEKHOV, ANTON (1860-1904)
Rothschild's Fiddle and Thirteen Other Stories (31)
CHESTERTON, G. K. (1874-   )
The Man Who Was Thursday (35)
CONTEMPORARY SCIENCE (99)
Edited with an Introduction by Dr. BENJ. HARROW
CRANE, STEPHEN (1870-1900)
Men, Women and Boats (102)
Introduction by VINCENT STARRETT

Modern Library of the World's Best Books

Modern Library of the World's Best Books

Modern Library of the World's Best Books

Modern Library of the World's Best Books

A Subject Index of Titles in

THE MODERN LIBRARY

FICTION

The Seven That Were Hanged, The Red Laugh, etc.—Andreyev
Rezanov—Atherton
The Way of All Flesh—Samuel Butler
The Man Who Was Thursday—Chesterton
The Flame of Life—D'Annunzio
The Triumph of Death—D'Annunzio
Sapho—Daudet
Poor People—Dostoyevsky
Madame Bovary—Flaubert
The Crime of Sylvestre Bonnard—Anatole France
Daisy Miller and An International Episode—James
Sons and Lovers—D. H Lawrence
Mme. Chrysantheme—Loti
Une Vie—Maupassant
Diana of the Crossways—Meredith
Married—Strindberg
Dame Care—Sudermann
Fathers and Sons—Turgenev
Smoke—Turgenev
The Red Lily—Anatole France
The Queen Pedauque—Anatole France
Thais—Anatole France
The Temptation of St. Anthony—Flaubert
Jorn Uhl—Frenssen
Mlle. de Maupin—Gautier
A Bed of Roses—W. L. George

Renee Mauperin—de Goncourt
The Mayor of Casterbridge—Hardy
Erik Dorn—Ben Hecht
Green Mansions—W. H. Hudson
The Cabin—Ibanez
In a Winter City—Ouida
Manon Lescaut—Prevost
An Unsocial Socialist—George Bernard Shaw
The Belfry—May Sinclair
Mary, Mary—James Stephens
Treasure Island—Stevenson
Candide—Voltaire
Ann Veronica—H. G. Wells
The War in the Air—H. G. Wells
Dorian Gray—Wilde
Private Papers of Henry Ryecroft—Gissing

SHORT STORIES

Winesburg, Ohio—Anderson
Balzac's Short Stories
Best Ghost Stories
Best American Humorous Short Stories
Best Russian Short Stories
Rothschild's Fiddle and Other Stories—Chekhov
Men, Women and Boats—Stephen Crane
Free and Other Stories—Theodore Dreiser
A Dreamer's Tales—Dunsany
Book of Wonder—Dunsany
Creatures That Once Were Men and Other Stories—Gorky

A Subject Index of Titles in
THE MODERN LIBRARY

French Romances in the
MODERN LIBRARY

In no other country has the novel of romance and love come to so fragrant and colorful a flowering as in France. Love in all its troubled currents of sorrow, its pulsing courses of pleasure, its flood-tides of exaltation, has been more sympathetically understood and more lucidly revealed by the great writers of France than by the writers of almost every other country. Not only has France universalized the word "amour," she has also revealed to us through her great novels, the very body and heart-beat of love.

Love and Other Stories— Guy De Maupassant

Crime of Sylvestre Bonnard —Anatole France

The Red Lily— Anatole France

Madame Bovary— Gustave Flaubert

Mlle. Fifi and Other Stories —Guy De Maupassant

Mlle. de Maupin— Theophile Gautier

Candide—Voltaire

The Queen Pedauque— Anatole France

Une Vie—Guy De Maupassant

Thais—Anatole France

Renee Mauperin—E. and J. de Goncourt

Sapho—Alphonse Daudet and **Manon Lescaut — **Antoine Francois Prevost (the two in one volume)

Madame Chrysantheme— Pierre Loti

Modern Library of the World's Best Books

Russian Literature in the
MODERN LIBRARY

The world has always regarded the Russian as some mysterious creature—half child, half genius. Out of Russia's soil has come a people, full of brooding, human pity and swift intuitions—a people sustained by the dreams of its idealists and brutalized by its despots. It is the soul of this creature half child, half genius, set against a background of racial hopes and sorrows, that the great writers of Russia have revealed to us in a literature that stands with the greatest literatures of the world.

The Seven That Were Hanged and The Red Laugh—Leonid Andreyev

Best Russian Short Stories —Edited by Thomas Seltzer

Rothschild's F i d d l e and Other Stories— Anton Chekhov

Poor People— Fiodor Dostoyevsky

Creatures That Once Were Men and Other Stories— Maxim Gorky

Redemption and Other Plays —Leo Tolstoy

The Death of Ivan Ilyitch and Other Stories— Leo Tolstoy

Fathers and Sons— Ivan Turgenev

Smoke—Ivan Turgenev

Distinguished Writers Who Have Written Introductions to Titles in the MODERN LIBRARY

In order to make each book in the Modern Library authoritative and helpful, we have, wherever possible, provided illuminating introductions by distinguished writers who are best qualified to write on their subject. These introductions are by some of the greatest writers and critics in the world. Of those who have written introductions to the Modern Library titles are such distinguished names as:

Ernest Boyd
James Branch Cabell
G. K. Chesterton
Padraic Colum
Clarence Day, Jr.
Floyd Dell
Ashley Dukes
Waldo Frank
John Galsworthy
Dr. Benjamin Harrow
Albert Bushnell Hart
Lafcadio Hearn
Guy Holt
Arthur Hopkins
Wm. Dean Howells
Henry James
Alexander Jessup
Joyce Kilmer
Richard Le Gallienne
Ludwig Lewisohn
Phillip Littell
John Macy
H. L. Mencken

Paul Elmer More
George Jean Nathan
John Payne
Burton Rascoe
John Reed
William Marion Reedy
Arthur B. Reeve
Ernest Rhys
Edgar Saltus
Carl Sandburg
T. B. Saunders
Thomas Seltzer
Vincent Starrett
Clifford Smyth
Arthur Symons
John Garrett Underhill
Carl Van Doren
Hendrik W. Van Loon
J. S. Van Teslaar
Carl Van Vechten
Willard Huntington Wright
Emile Zola

Printed in the United Kingdom
by Lightning Source UK Ltd.
119334UK00001B/333